ALL ABOUT me

ALL ABOUT ME

Text by Anna Prudente-Poulton

An Hachette UK Company
www.hachette.co.uk

Vie Books, an imprint of Summersdale Publishers Ltd
Part of Octopus Publishing Group Limited
Carmelite House
50 Victoria Embankment
LONDON
EC4Y 0DZ
UK

www.summersdale.com

Printed and bound in China

ISBN: 978-1-80007-554-2

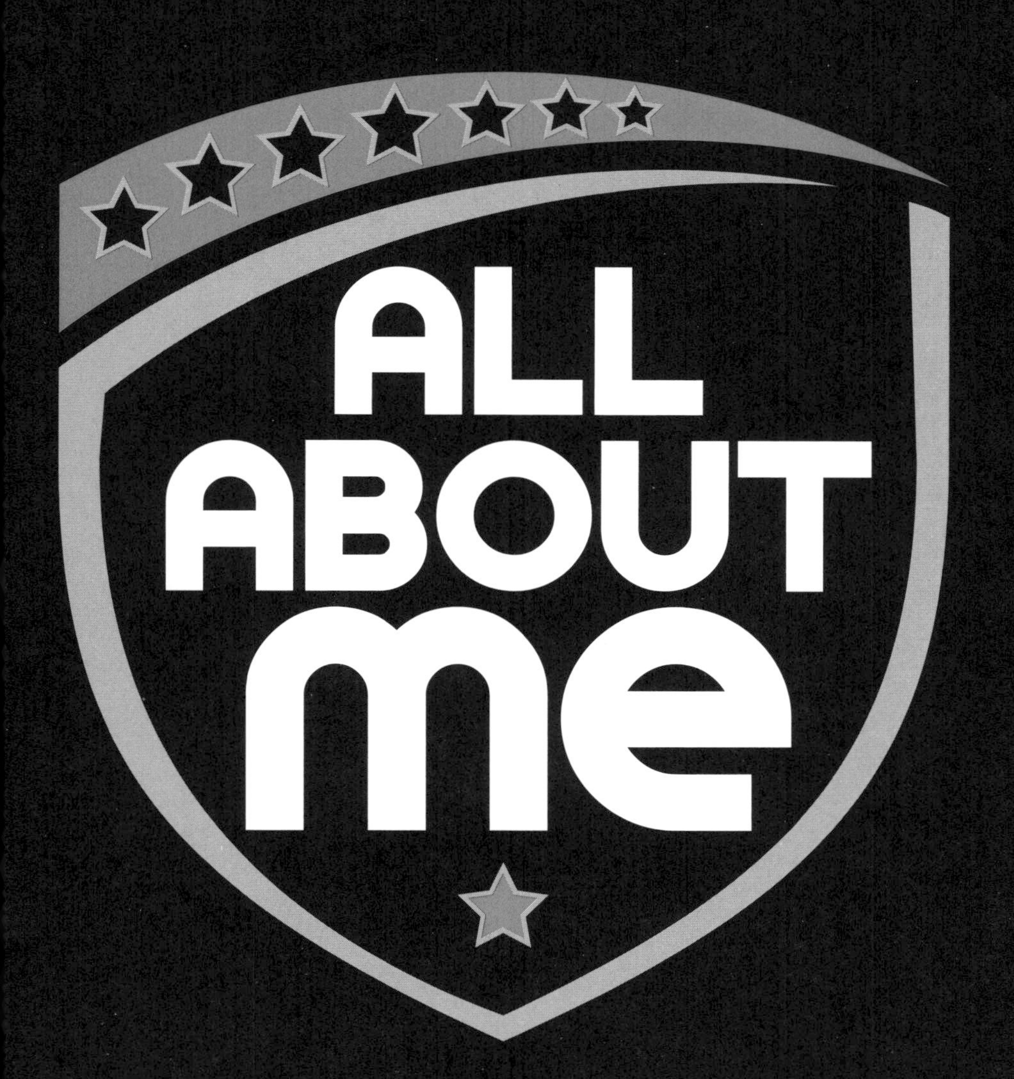

An awesome self-discovery journal for boys

To★★★★★★★★★★★★★★★★★★★★★★★★★★★★★★★★

From★★★★★★★★★★★★★★★★★★★★★★★★★★

Contents

Introduction

Hi there! You are growing up through a period of transformation on fast forward and it can feel overwhelming at times. This book will guide you to a better understanding of yourself and equip you with superpowers, so that you can deal with your thoughts, tempers and friendships. But fundamentally, crack on with the quizzes, tips and activities and have a laugh!

Recharge your mojo when you read, share and scribble your way through these pages, stuffed with tips, activities, quizzes and quotes. Let your awesomeness shine through!

All About Me will give you the boost you need to feel courageous, confident and resilient. Words have power and what you write, you will feel and what you feel, you believe!

Ready? Let's begin!

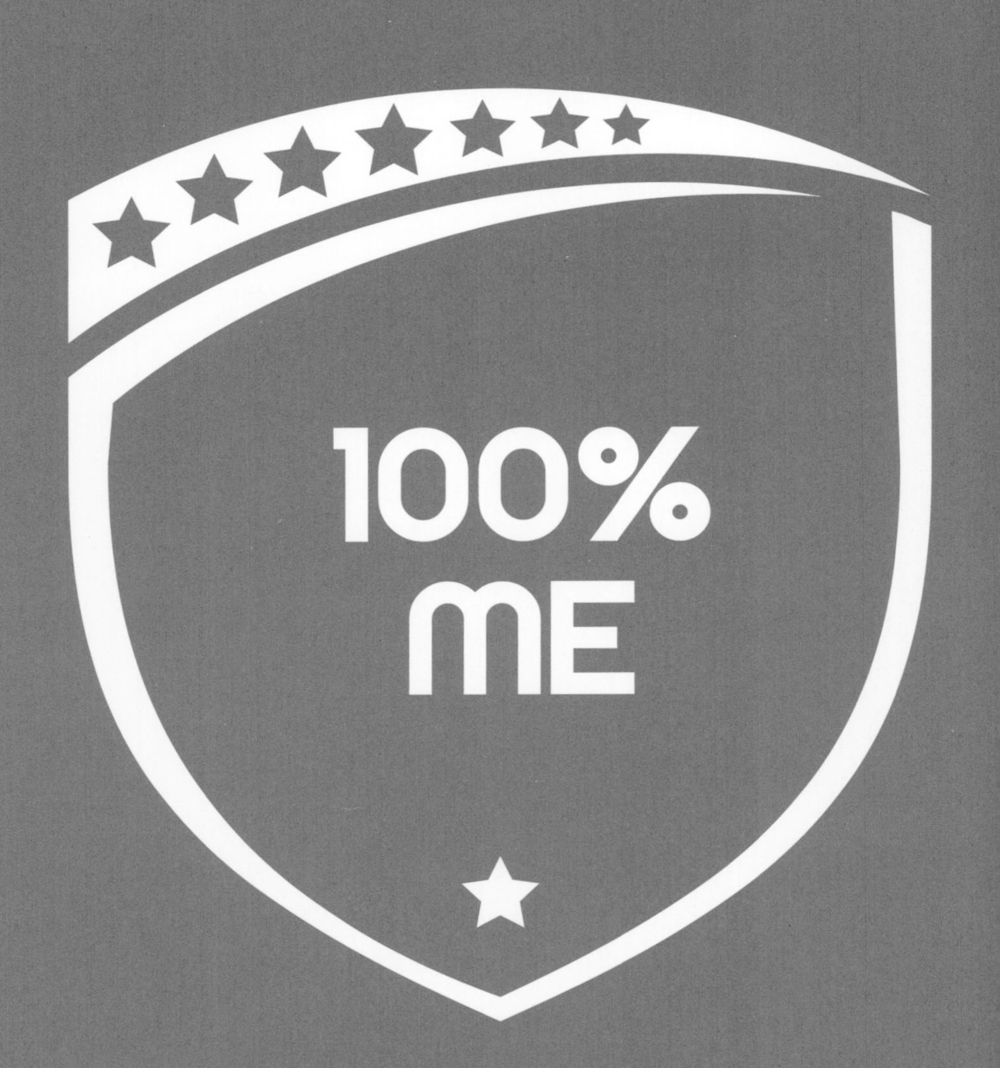

CHAPTER ONE

It's no secret that you're an exceptional person. This first chapter will challenge you to think carefully about the qualities that make you uniquely *you* and give you the lowdown on how to be your very best self!

My name is

____

My nickname is

____

I support __________________________ (sports team)

I support __________________________ (sports team)

I support __________________________ (sports team)

My favourite film at the moment is

____

My favourite music at the moment is

____

My favourite book at the moment is

____

My birthday is ______________________________

The place I was born is called ____________________ in the country of ____________________ on the planet Earth, in the Milky Way, in an ever-expanding universe!

My star sign is ______________________________

I am ____________ years old.

My parents are called ____________________ and ____________________

I have ____________ brother/s and ____________ sister/s.

His/Her/Their name/s is/are ______________________________

____

My school is called

____

I rate the following sports in order of preference: football, cricket, hockey, rugby, tennis, American football, baseball

1 ______________________

2 ______________________

3 ______________________

4 ______________________

5 ______________________

6 ______________________

7 ______________________

My friends are

____

____

____

I have  pets.

1 is a ____________________ called ____________________

2 is a ____________________ called ____________________

3 is a ____________________ called ____________________

4 is a ____________________ called ____________________

5 is a ____________________ called ____________________

At the moment, I would like to be ____________________________ when I'm older.

I was given this book on ____

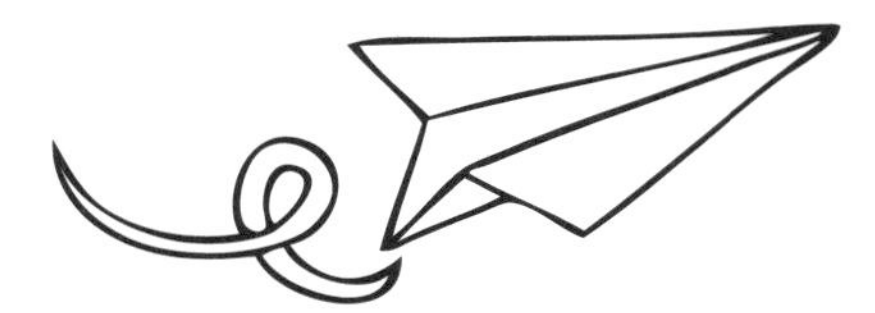

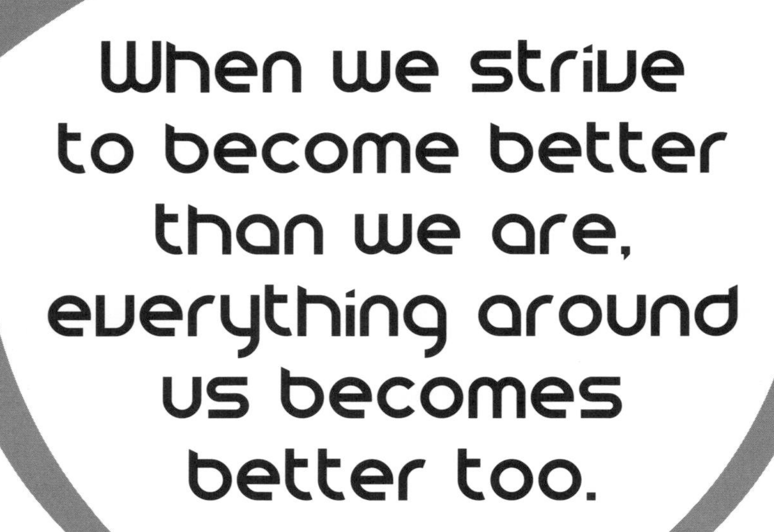

PAULO COELHO

Sleepy Secrets!

What does your sleep style say about the real you?

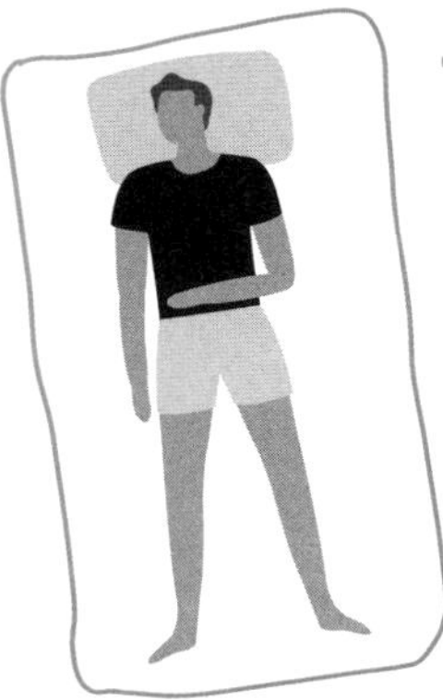

The Soldier Position

You're a thoughtful, calm person, valuing time alone. You can be a perfectionist and have very high expectations. You hate laziness but remember to chill with friends!

The Foetal Position

You are warm and generous. You are tough on the outside but caring on the inside. You're very lucky to have a close-knit set of friends and family, with whom you can be yourself.

The Freefall Position

Wow! It's surprising you get any sleep with your social life! You have loads of friends and you love to stay active. But you can be very moody and you do have to watch that temper of yours!

Who are you?

Answer these to gain a deeper understanding of who you are and what makes you awesome!

1. What five words do you think best describe you?

2. What do you like doing that makes you feel happiest?

3. What do you know how to do that you can teach others?

4. What is the most wonderful thing that has ever happened to you?

5. What is the worst thing that has ever happened to you?

6. Of all the things you are learning, what do you think will be the most useful when you are an adult?

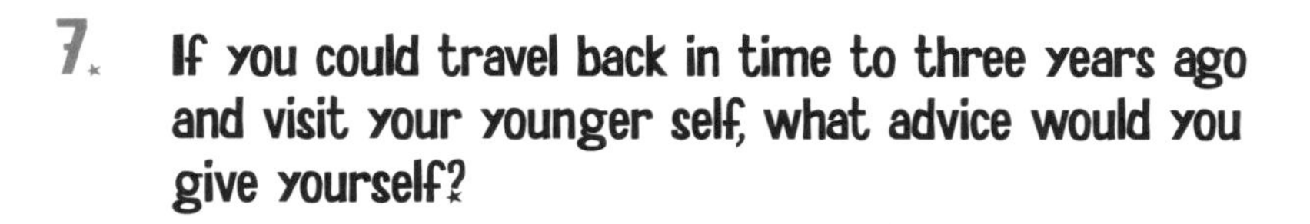

7. If you could travel back in time to three years ago and visit your younger self, what advice would you give yourself?

8. What are you most grateful for?

9. What do you think your life will be like in the future?

10. If you could grow up to be famous, what would you want to be famous for?

11. How would you change the world if you could?

12. How can you help someone today?

13. If you could make one rule that everyone in the world had to follow, what rule would you make and why?

TEAM

!

So many of you out there will know instinctively who to write in the space above and who to cheer on from the stands or in front of the TV. But I suspect there are some who haven't fully committed to a team. Perhaps they only recently developed an interest in their sport because of a national or international competition? Maybe their family aren't sports fans, or they just don't ally themselves to a particular team.

Being a sports fan is a "very psychologically healthy activity," says Daniel Wann, professor at Murray State University, whose research centres on the psychology of sport fandom. Fandom connects us to other like-minded people, which satisfies our human need for belonging. Sports fans have higher self-esteem and are more satisfied with their lives (whether their teams win or lose).

So follow one of these approaches to track down your team!

Choose your team based on where you currently live.

- Many people support their local team. This is perhaps the simplest and easiest way to pick a team to support. The benefit of this approach is that many of your friends and family will probably also support the same one. This will make matches more fun.

- If your city or town does not have a team, what big city with a team are you closest to?
- If you are equal distance to two teams, pick whichever you prefer, or whichever one your friends and family support; they are bound to have a healthy rivalry, however, so bear that in mind!

Support the team of the city or region where you were born (if different).

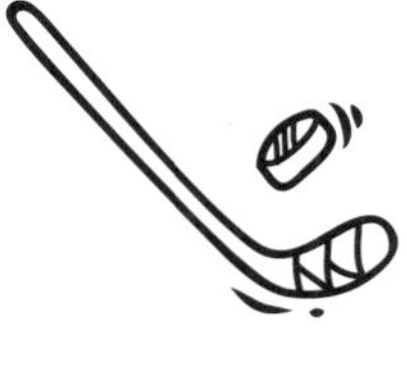

- Some people are lifelong supporters of one team. They support the team of their home town where they grew up, and stick with it for the rest of their lives. You can go with this approach as well.
- This will help you bond with family and friends who still live in that community, if you have moved.

Rally behind the team your parents or siblings support.

- For many families, supporting a sports team is tradition. Get behind that tradition and support the same team as your parents and grandparents. If your family is not united around a team, start the tradition!

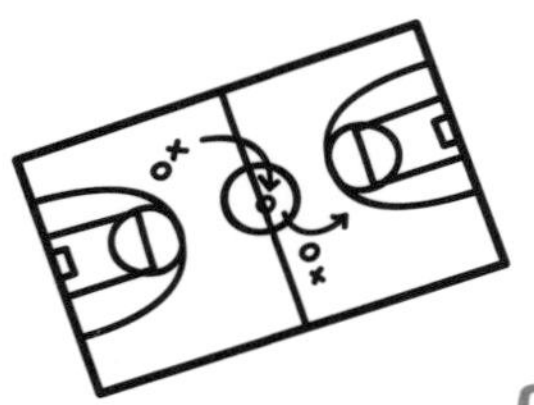

Consider the mascot or team colours.

- Some people are attracted by mascots and team colours. If this sounds like you, start researching the wide variety of mascots and team colours of different teams around the country. On the other hand, you might not like a team's mascot or colours, so you can easily eliminate them from your potential list.

Support the underdog.

- You might be the sort of person who likes supporting the underdog. In this case, look at a few teams that have been struggling in recent years. This can be fun, too, since a lot of people tend to support winners. When your team wins, you'll have a lot more to celebrate.

Pick a team based on an individual player or coach/manager.

- Perhaps an individual player or coach/manager impresses you. This is an alternative way of picking a team to support. You can choose to follow that player or coach/manager, and you'll be invested in a career and in someone's talent.

Cheer for the winning team.

- A lot of people like to support teams that are currently winning. These teams are more likely to have very talented coaching staff and players, which is a big draw for a lot of people.

Remember!

- Don't base your preference on skill level. That's not everything!
- Choose for yourself and no one else.

- Remember, you can always change your team.
- Don't leave your team if they perform badly for one season. Give them some time to get better and stick with them.

We all want to be the hero and now you can.
Draw yourself in your very own comic strip!

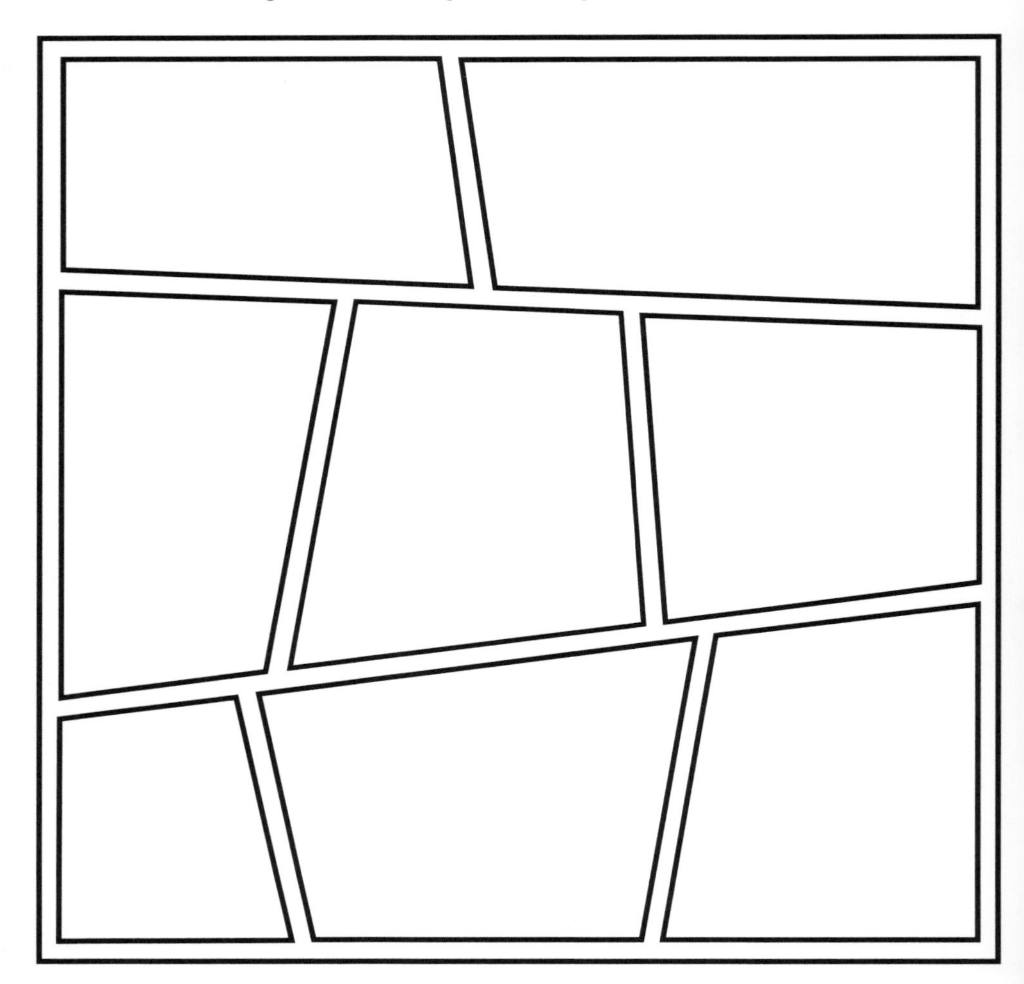

You have a ton of homework, you're arguing with your sister, your phone's ringing but you're expected downstairs for supper. **Arrggh!!**

Take a deep breath, as this will begin to calm you, and focus by recording exactly what you are doing in this moment in time...

Date:
Time:
Place:
What can you smell?
What sounds can you hear?
What are you wearing?
What is the weather like?
What can you see?
Are you with anyone?
What can you feel?
How do you feel?

I hope that you are feeling calmer and more focused and attentive. This is a simple mindfulness meditation – paying attention to what is immediately around you and what is happening in the present moment.

PERSONALITY PROFILE!

Have you always wondered what your friends really think of you? Find out by answering these questions together – truthfully!

1) What do you like the most about your friend?

a) You never know what they are going to do next!

b) They're always first to know what's going on.

c) They totally get you.

d) You can rely on them.

2) Which do you find the most annoying?

a) Having to follow pointless rules.

b) Being grounded.

c) Someone lying to you.

d) Being rushed into decision-making.

3) A friend calls you and they're obviously upset. Do you...

a) Listen to them and try to reason with them?

b) Arrange to take them out to distract them?

c) Offer to head straight over?

d) Try to offer practical help?

4) How would your mum describe you?

a) A nightmare around the house!

b) A bit messy.

c) Calm and helpful.

d) Very organized.

5) During lunch break, what do you usually do?

a) Mess around in the art room.

b) Just hang in a big group.

c) Have a one-on-one with a mate.

d) Flick through your phone.

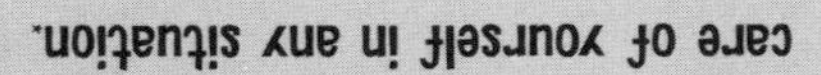

Mostly a): You're creative and unconventional and you hate following rules. You think with your heart and go with your gut!

Mostly b): You're a geezer! You have loads of friends and have loads of confidence.

Mostly c): You're a caring friend and always there when needed. You prefer to be with people you love and trust.

Mostly d): You're very practical and down-to-earth and can take care of yourself in any situation.

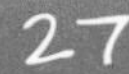

CALM THOSE QUALMS

Everyone worries but sometimes our worries grow and feel overpowering. We may start biting our nails and getting grumpy with our family. We may have stomach aches and feel sick, need the loo more often and feel hot and sweaty. This is when we need to *breathe*.

We all breathe without thinking about it but focusing on our breath going into – and then out of – our bodies significantly calms us down.

- Try to find somewhere as calm and quiet as possible.
- Close your mouth and slowly breathe into your lungs, so that you can see your stomach rising. When you feel that you can't take any more, slowly breathe out through your mouth so you can hear yourself breathing. Try this until you feel calmer.
- Try your hardest to pin down your worries and write them down, on paper or in a diary or journal. If you don't feel that you can talk to someone about your worries yet, then you can either rip or screw up the paper and bury it in a place that's meaningful to you. The simple act of taking worries out of your head onto paper helps put them in perspective.

Top Tip

Some people find it hard to breathe deep into their lungs at first, as they are used to shallow breathing. If you lie face down on the floor and fold your arms underneath your head, it's impossible to breathe any other way!

Anxiety's like
a rocking chair.
It gives you
something to do,
but it doesn't
get you very far.

Jodi Picoult

A spotter's guide

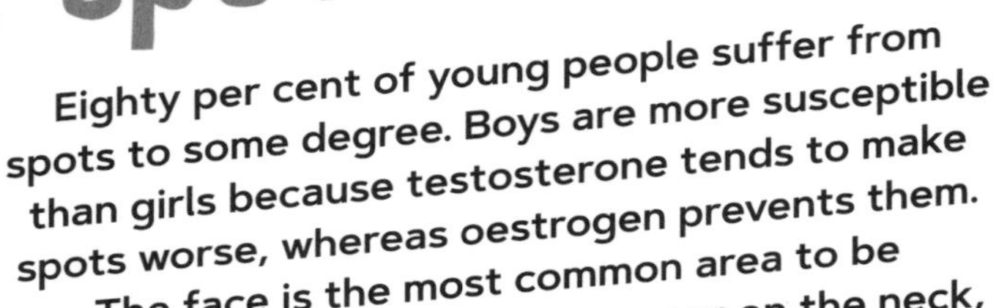

Eighty per cent of young people suffer from spots to some degree. Boys are more susceptible than girls because testosterone tends to make spots worse, whereas oestrogen prevents them. The face is the most common area to be affected, but spots can also appear on the neck, upper back, shoulders and chest.

Don't Believe the Myths!

There are many myths about what causes spots. Yet, contrary to what you may have heard, spots are not caused by having a dirty face or eating foods like chocolate or French fries.

It's tough when you're breaking out and some of your friends have clear skin, but it's not your fault that you have spots. Spots are triggered by hormonal changes during puberty, not by outside influences. Thanks to genetics, some people are just naturally more prone to developing pimples.

Take Care of Your Skin Every Day

Even though spots aren't caused by neglecting to wash your face, the excess oil and dirt that builds up throughout the day won't help matters. Sweat can also irritate your skin and make spots worse. That is why a good skin care routine is important.

It only takes a few minutes a day and doesn't require a ton of fancy products. All you need is basic face soap and cleanser, and a moisturizer if your skin is feeling dry.

If you are worried, then ask a grown-up to help you find a suitable spot or acne treatment – they can be found in most chemists and supermarkets. If you feel that your spots are getting worse, then ask a grown-up to take you to your doctor.

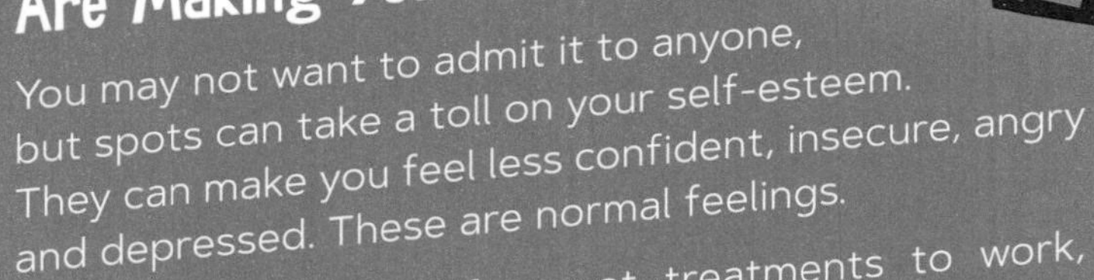

Tell Somebody If Spots Are Making You Feel Down

You may not want to admit it to anyone, but spots can take a toll on your self-esteem. They can make you feel less confident, insecure, angry and depressed. These are normal feelings.

While you're waiting for spot treatments to work, distract yourself with sports, music, art or any other interests you have.

There will likely be times when you just can't seem to *not* think about spots. If they're making you feel down, let someone know. Tell your parents, a favourite teacher, your healthcare provider, or anyone you trust.

You can get through it, you can get over it, and you can feel good about your skin and yourself again.

CRAFTY, EH?

Want to make a spot-busting miracle formula? OK, so it's lavender water but it honestly works and it's basically free!

Choose a time you haven't got much on and have a go.

You will need...

A saucepan

A measuring jug

Fresh or dried lavender flowers

A plastic, wooden or ceramic bowl

A fine sieve or piece of muslin (very fine cloth sold in kitchenware shops)

A glass bottle, preferably green or brown

- Bring 100 ml water up to a fast boil. (Maybe ask an older sibling or grown-up to help you.)
- Pour this over two tablespoons of fresh or dried lavender flowers in a non-metallic bowl.
- Cover the bowl and leave at room temperature until it is cool, or overnight.
- Strain the mixture using a fine sieve or piece of muslin.
- Pour into a very clean glass bottle (ideally dark-coloured) and keep it in the fridge.

Use it on your skin every night and help erase those spots for good!

BE STRONG ENOUGH

to stand alone,

SMART ENOUGH

to know when you need help

AND BRAVE ENOUGH

to ask for it.

HOW FEARLESS ARE YOU?

Would you ever... (or maybe you have?!)

hold a tarantula?

☐ a) of course! ☐ b) maybe ☐ c) I don't think so

go on a night hike?

☐ a) of course! ☐ b) maybe ☐ c) I don't think so

do a skydive?

☐ a) of course! ☐ b) maybe ☐ c) I don't think so

go on a roller coaster?

☐ a) of course! ☐ b) maybe ☐ c) I don't think so

do a bungee jump?

☐ a) of course! ☐ b) maybe ☐ c) I don't think so

swim with sharks?

☐ a) of course! ☐ b) maybe ☐ c) I don't think so

stay in a well-known haunted place?

☐ a) of course! ☐ b) maybe ☐ c) I don't think so

learn to fly a plane?

☐ a) of course! ☐ b) maybe ☐ c) I don't think so

have a snake wrapped around your neck?

☐ a) of course! ☐ b) maybe ☐ c) I don't think so

ride a motorbike?

☐ a) of course! ☐ b) maybe ☐ c) I don't think so

Mostly a): You never turn down a dare, and are always up for whatever challenge comes your way. But don't take it too far – stay safe!

Mostly b): You're not afraid to try new things but you always think it through beforehand.

Mostly c): You like to play it safe and are always the first to stop your friends from getting into trouble. But don't be too afraid of trying new things!

Don't think about it too much but sign your name in the box below:

Now do a doodle – the first thing that comes in your head – in the box below:

Your signature

If your signature is large and fills the box, you're a very outgoing person who loves to be the centre of attention.

If your signature is small with lots of space around it, you're very thoughtful and enjoy spending time on your own.

Doodle!

If you've doodled eyes or plants, then you're caring, kind and thoughtful. Geometric shapes can mean that you are very organized and good at planning. Patterns can mean you have lots of energy, are creative and pay attention to detail. People and animals suggest that you are warm and friendly and you don't like being alone.

Spiralling

If you began at the outside of the spiral and drew the spiral toward the centre, then you tend to look at the bigger picture and sort out the details afterward. If you began at the centre of the spiral and drew outward, then you tend to focus on the details first.

What makes you tick?

A diary with a difference...

Perhaps you already know what fires you up and keeps you on maximum power all week, but many aren't so lucky. Some of you probably haven't discovered your passions yet so this tracker might help you. Answer each question every day for a month and you may be surprised by what is revealed!

a) What did you do today that you'd love to do every day?

b) Did something make you laugh?

c) What was the best thing that happened?

d) Did you find out anything interesting?

e) What made you smile?

Month ________ Year ________

DAY	A	B	C	D	E
1					
2					
3					
4					
5					
6					
7					
8					
9					
10					
11					
12					
13					
14					
15					
16					
17					
18					
19					
20					
21					
22					
23					
24					
25					
26					
27					
28					
29					
30					
31					

TAKE CARE!

TAKE CARE OF YOUR BODY:

- **Exercise regularly.** Make sure you get your heart rate up for at least 30 minutes every day. This can be through running, playing sport or even walking fast.
- **Eat a healthy diet.** Healthy eating is an important part of your growth and development. Eat plenty of fruit and vegetables, wholegrains and a variety of protein foods.
- **Get enough sleep.** You really need an average of nine hours of sleep every night, but many average only seven hours. Sleep has a powerful effect on your ability to concentrate and perform at school, excel in sport and maintain a social life.
- **Brush and floss your teeth.** Make it a habit now, and prevent tooth and gum problems in adulthood.
- **Wear sunscreen.** Getting just one bad sunburn as a child or teenager increases your risk of developing skin cancer as an adult.

DON'T FORGET THE REST OF YOU!

- **Learn ways to stay calm in tough situations.** There are tips in this book to help you.
- **Study and try your best in school.** There is a strong link between health and doing as well as you can in school.
- **Try to get on with your parents!** They can be so frustrating sometimes but remember all that they want is the best for you. Try to see where they are coming from when they set rules.

FINALLY, TAKE CARE OF YOUR FEELINGS!

- **Pay attention to your moods and feelings.** Don't assume your negative thoughts or feelings are just part of life or being a pre-teen. If you're worried about something, ask for help.

- **Don't be afraid to ask for help if you need it.** If you feel that you can't talk to your parents, talk to a favourite teacher or counsellor at school. Find an adult you can trust. If you're feeling really sad or are thinking about harming yourself, get help right away.

- **Accept yourself.** If you feel like you have low self-esteem or a poor body image, talk to someone about it. Even just talking to a friend can help.
- **Speak up.** If you are being bullied, tell a parent, teacher or other adult. This includes being bullied online or on your phone.

CHAPTER TWO

Life is complicated for you right now; you are negotiating puberty, making new friends, starting a new school – and then there's exams added to this heady mix! But don't worry – you've got this!

Read on for tips and quizzes on some of the big questions you face in your life now.

School hacks

You will have enough rules at school to cope with but don't rule these out!

- Always eat some breakfast, even if you feel nervous. It's a long time until lunch. Food really helps your concentration and stops you from feeling tired in your lessons.
- Put in plenty of practice at tying your tie or your shoe laces. You'll need to be able to do it at speed and under pressure (for example, after sports).
- If you'll need to use a travel pass, make sure your grown-ups apply for it in plenty of time – it may take a couple of weeks to come through, so don't leave it until the end of the holidays. And make sure there's money on it if you need it.
- Get some passport photos taken – they're useful for a travel pass or library card.
- Work out your route to school, whether you're walking or taking public transport.
- Make sure you have a strong bag. You may have loads to carry. And that's not counting the days when you'll have your sports kit.
- If you can, find a friend to walk with on your first day. Things won't seem so daunting if you can go with someone.
- Be prepared to just "hang out" at playtime. *Don't call it "playtime" – it's "break" now!*
- Work out how you'll be paying for your lunch – if it's a card or fingerprint system, make sure you've been topped up for your first day.

- Try not to eat pizza every day.
- Find out where the toilets are.
- Find out your new school's policy on mobile phones, preferably before yours goes off in the middle of geography.
- When you are given your timetable, make at least three copies: one for your bag, one for your pocket and a spare for home.
- Get your new friends' phone numbers – you may need to give them a call if you have a last-minute homework panic.
- Find out all you can about your new friends. Your mum is bound to ask!
- Be organized. If you're given a student diary or planner, use it to write down your homework – when there is so much going on, it's easy to forget.
- Go through your timetable and pack your bag the night before – there's never time in the morning to find your maths book.
- Never be afraid to ask for help if you're not sure where to go.
- At lesson changeover, stick with someone who knows where they're going. And don't try to go against the flow of traffic – you'll only be trampled.

Relax and try to enjoy it – in no time at all, it'll seem like you've been there forever. And this time next year, you'll be showing the newbies around the school.

ANONYMOUS

Booked up!

Write down ten books that you have loved recently. Then put them into a list according to how much you liked them and how memorable they are. If you haven't been reading much lately, write down ten books you would like to get around to reading in the future!

1)	1st
2)	2nd
3)	3rd
4)	4th
5)	5th
6)	6th
7)	7th
8)	8th
9)	9th
10)	10th

Sports Trivia Tournament

This is for you and your mates: play in teams and make a night of it! Which one of your mates is triv-tastic? Who will get to be crowned the Sports King?

1) Who is England's most capped football player to date?
2) Which woman has won the most Grand Slam tennis titles to date?

3) Who is Britain's most decorated Olympian to date?
4) Who was the first person to run a four-minute mile?
5) How many players make up the Ryder Cup?
6) Where is the World Darts Championship famously held every year?

7) What is the diameter of a basketball hoop in inches?
8) What's the national sport of Canada?
9) How many dimples does the average golf ball have?
10) In motor racing, what colour is the flag they wave to indicate the winner?
11) How long is a marathon?
12) What is the only sport to have been played on the moon?

13) In which winter sport are the terms "stale fish" and "mule kick" used?

14) What team is considered the oldest in the NFL?

15) Who is the world's most capped player in rugby to date?

16) Who is UK Cricket's all-time top run scorer to date?

17) Who is the Premier League's all-time top scorer to date?

18) Which WWE superstar did Tyson Fury wrestle in 2019?

19) Which NFL team has the record of scoring the most points in a single Super Bowl to date?

20) Who was the first NBA player to shatter a backboard?

Answers:

1) Peter Shilton
2) Serena Williams
3) Jason Kenny
4) Roger Bannister
5) Each team has 12 players to choose from for a total of 28 games to be played
6) Alexandra Palace
7) 18 inches
8) Lacrosse
9) 336
10) Black and white (chequered flag)
11) 26.2 miles
12) Golf
13) Snowboarding
14) Green Bay Packers
15) Alun Wyn Jones
16) Alastair Cook
17) Alan Shearer
18) Braun Strowman
19) The San Francisco 49ers
20) Chuck Connors

Switch Off

You must be sick of hearing your parents and teachers drone on about the amount of time you spend on screens. But why don't you just spend a few minutes looking at good and not-so-good aspects of screen time yourself?

Too much screen time can prevent you from being with friends offline and spending time with family. It may also damage your ability to focus and make sleeping difficult.

Essentially, if your screen time is replacing time needed for sleeping, eating, being active, studying and interacting with family and friends, then you should seriously think about reducing it.

If you do these few things every day, you will begin to feel more rested, have higher energy levels and feel happier.

- Leave your smartphone/devices downstairs at night, and perhaps listen to a book or music through a smart speaker. The light from mobile phones delays and reduces sleep, and can cause headaches and confusion.
- Try to be physically active for at least 30 minutes every day.
- Join a club or two (sports or otherwise). There will be loads available in your area – including ones organized by your school.
- Put your smartphone/devices down while you're eating.
- Whether you're watching Netflix or playing on your Switch, try to do one thing at a time: second or third screening is well known to be hazardous for your concentration and focus.

No Posting.
No Liking.
No Sharing.
Just Living.

Savvy on social!

So, you've heard this all before but try to remember that what you post online, stays online. This makes it an important aspect of your life today and you do need to understand the dangers, as well as enjoying all the benefits the internet brings.

Although most of the social networking sites require you to be 13 before you can join, there are a few that allow younger kids – like Roblox – and it is never too early to learn how to be a savvy socializer!

Social media can negatively affect you by distracting you, disrupting your sleep, and exposing you to bullying, rumour spreading, unrealistic views of other people's lives and peer pressure. That's a lot of things!

Before you roll your eyes, the following guidelines are purely for protection, not stopping you from having fun or limiting your freedom. You don't want to be ripped off, bullied, disrespected, scammed or worse, while you're just trying to have a good time online.

Keep out!

The best place to start is to check your privacy settings. In most cases, the default privacy settings will give your posts the most public exposure where strangers can see them. You can post sensitive information without even realizing it, for example, a photo with an identifiable background. In a nutshell, keep your social profile strictly private – just allow access to your friends and family.

Be cautious of friend requests

Obvious I know, but friend requests from strangers can often turn out to be spam bots (meaning you'll be spamming your friends). Fake profiles are also created for cyberbullying. So even when a new friend request comes in, and you think you know the person, be sure to check their profile first and see if anything looks fishy.

Pause before you post!

Never give away your phone number or address; if you want to share this information with a friend, do it directly by phone, text or in person.

Be aware that even though you can delete something (a post, picture, comment, etc.) on your devices, you can never permanently erase something that has been published on the internet.

The most important thing to remember is that if you do make a mistake, such as posting something you didn't intend or seeing something online you shouldn't have seen, tell a trusted adult: you will never be in trouble, but they will want to make sure that you are OK.

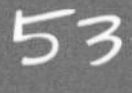

Boot it!

The first step in your confident and happy life is to try to worry less, as worrying can hold you back. In each football, write down your five biggest worries for the year ahead and imagine kicking that football off the pitch and out of sight!

Then keep returning to this page and, if any of your worries has become smaller or has disappeared, then draw a football in the goal.

Branch out!

There are many reasons to make your own family tree:

- It helps you feel more connected to your heritage.
- It brings history to life when you learn about your family history in relation to historical events.
- As you learn more about your ancestors, you will enjoy preserving family stories and traditions.
- It can be fun!

How do you make a simple family tree?

Gather information about your family. Write down what you know, ask family members to fill in the gaps, and find pictures and documents. Begin to fill in the tree that is provided for you over the page.

Your family tree

Great grand parent?
Great grand parent?
1983 – The video game *Mario Bros.* is first released as a Nintendo arcade game in Japan.
Grand parent?
Grand parent?
1961 – The Soviet cosmonaut Yuri Gagarin becomes the first person in space.
Sibling?
Parent?
You
Sibling?

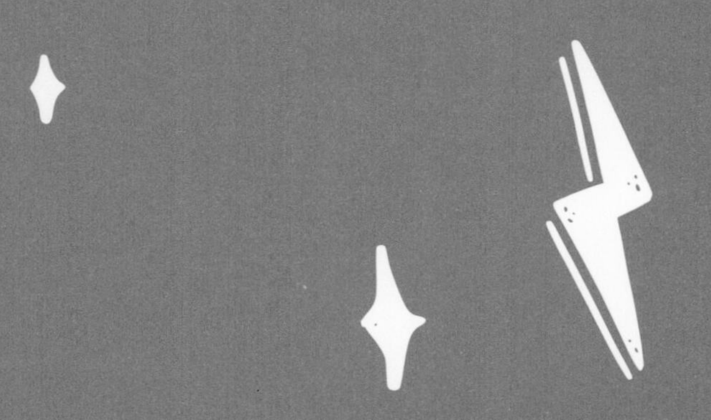

Never forget about the people you love.

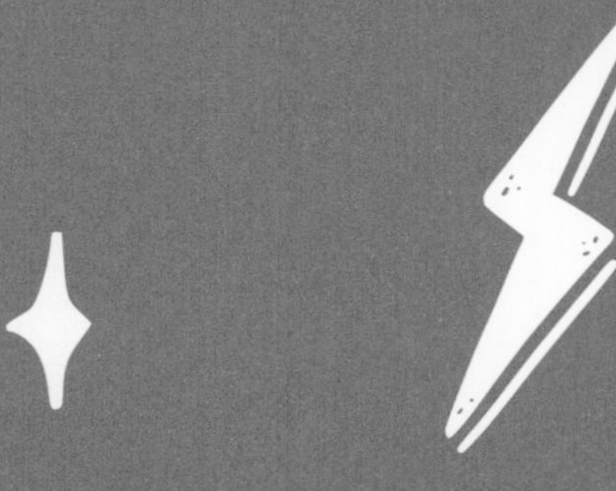

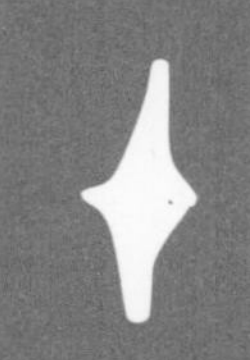

Meditative Moments

You can benefit greatly from meditation. It allows you to focus on the present and forget about your worries and everything else going on in your life for a moment.

THOUGHT HUNTER

Sit still with your eyes closed and count slowly from one to ten. If any thought comes into your mind, immediately go back to one. Watch for even the smallest thought, even a sound, even the thought "I'm already at number three". This is the first step in being able to quieten your mind and have a break from any annoying thoughts that might be troubling you. Do this until you feel calmer.

CLOSING THE SENSES

Place your thumbs in your ears so that you won't be able to hear anything, place your index fingers gently on your eyelids, place the middle fingers on your nose, the next set of fingers above your lips, and your little fingers under your lips. Breathe in for five counts and out for five, loudly, so that you can hear your breath very loudly inside your head. After about ten deep breaths, gradually make your breath very quiet and unnoticeable. Now, start listening to any sounds you can still hear, no matter how quiet. Stay like this for another few minutes before releasing your hands.

What's your top ten...?

Check out the lists then rate your top ten favourite things on the opposite page.

Bestselling video game series of all time

(Source: thegamer.com, Oct 2021)

1) Mario
2) Tetris
3) Call of Duty
4) Pokémon
5) Grand Theft Auto
6) Fifa
7) Minecraft
8) Wii Series
9) The Sims
10) Lego

Top ten best animals

(Source: thetoptens.com poll, 2021)

1) Dog
2) Cat
3) Wolf
4) Tiger
5) Dolphin
6) Penguin
7) Lion
8) Horse
9) Elephant
10) Fox

Top ten most streamed artists on Spotify

(Source: chartmasters.org, Jan 2022)

1) Drake
2) Ed Sheeran
3) Bad Bunny
4) Ariana Grande
5) The Weeknd
6) Justin Bieber
7) Post Malone
8) Eminem
9) Taylor Swift
10) J Balvin

Top ten natural wonders of the world

(Source: thetoptens.com poll, 2021)

1) Grand Canyon, USA
2) Great Barrier Reef, Australia
3) Niagara Falls, Canada
4) Caño Cristales, Columbia
5) Mount Everest, Nepal/China
6) Aurora Borealis (Northern Lights), Norway, Sweden, Finland, Russia, Canada, Greenland, Alaska
7) Amazon Rainforest, South America
8) Pamukkale, Turkey
9) Waitomo Glowworm Caves, New Zealand
10) Hạ Long Bay, Vietnam

Top ten coolest facts about the planet Mars

(Source: thetoptens.com poll, 2021)

1) Mars has the largest mountain in our solar system.
2) Mars has the largest canyon in our solar system.
3) There is water on Mars.
4) Mars might eventually get rings.
5) You can grow asparagus and turnips on Mars.
6) On Mars, sunsets are blue.
7) You would weigh less than half your weight on Mars.
8) A year on Mars is almost twice as long as a year on Earth.
9) Tuesday is the Day of Mars. When the ancient Babylonians first created the week and divided it into seven days, they named each day of the week after the seven known bodies in the sky: the Sun (Sunday), the Moon (Moon day or Monday), Mars, Mercury, Jupiter, Venus and Saturn (Saturday).
10) Mars has two moons.

The top ten highest-grossing movies of all time (Source: businessinsider.com, Nov 2021)

1) *Avatar*
2) *Avengers: Endgame*
3) *Titanic*
4) *Star Wars: The Force Awakens*
5) *Avengers: Infinity War*
6) *Jurassic World*
7) *The Lion King (2019)*
8) *Furious 7*
9) *The Avengers*
10) *Frozen II*

1. ______________________________
2. ______________________________
3. ______________________________
4. ______________________________
5. ______________________________
6. ______________________________
7. ______________________________
8. ______________________________
9. ______________________________
10. ______________________________

Motivation is what gets

YOU STARTED.

Habit is what keeps

YOU GOING.

Debrief over dinner

You see them every day and yet how much do you *actually* know about your parents?

1) How did your parents meet?
2) What colour are your dad's eyes?
3) For a summer break, would your mum prefer a luxury resort, a rustic mountain cabin, resting at home, or somewhere else?
4) Does your dad believe in aliens?
5) Does your mum believe in love at first sight?
6) Would your dad rather watch TV with the family, sit alone and read, or go out to dinner with friends?
7) How old was your mum on her first date?
8) If your dad turned on the TV and found these choices, which would he pick: a football game, soap opera, old movie, or turn off the set?
9) What was your dad's first full-time job?
10) Who is your mum's closest friend?
11) What gift would your dad most like to receive?
12) When your parents were your age, what did they want to be when they "grew up"?
13) What was your parents' favourite subject in school? Least favourite?
14) Does your mum fill the car with petrol as soon as the tank is half empty or when the fuel is nearly gone?
15) What was your mum's first full-time job?

Summary

If you got 15 right: Congratulations! You really know your parent(s).

If you got 11–14 right: Not bad but try to pay a little more attention.

Fewer than 11 right: You need a crash course called mum and dad 101!

ARE YOU A PROCRASTINATING PRO?

We're all allowed to put things off sometimes – because we're not in the right mood, have low energy levels or can't get off the sofa to turn off the TV! But if this becomes a habit, it can affect every aspect of our lives and can often mask underlying problems such as fear of failure or acute anxiety. This activity will help you determine if you have a procrastination problem.

I have difficulty getting out of the house on time in the morning.

- ☐ **Very often**
- ☐ **Often**
- ☐ **Sometimes**
- ☐ **Rarely**
- ☐ **Never**

Even when I have an important deadline, I start working at the very last minute.

- ☐ **Very often**
- ☐ **Often**
- ☐ **Sometimes**
- ☐ **Rarely**
- ☐ **Never**

When there's something important that needs to be done, I tend to find other things to do and waste time.

- ☐ **Very often**
- ☐ **Often**
- ☐ **Sometimes**
- ☐ **Rarely**
- ☐ **Never**

When I'm doing homework, I waste time by checking my email or social media sites.

☐ **Very often** ☐ **Often** ☐ **Sometimes**
☐ **Rarely** ☐ **Never**

When I go to bed at night, I am stressed about all the things that I did not achieve during the day.

☐ **Very often** ☐ **Often** ☐ **Sometimes**
☐ **Rarely** ☐ **Never**

Don't put off till tomorrow what you can do today!

If you answered often or very often to more than three of these questions, then you are well on your way to being a pro at procrastination. But don't worry! We have a couple of tips to help you.

The old phrase above is very wise and indicates that this isn't just a problem for you! You know that you are going to have to do this task at some point anyway, so why not now? It stops all the worrying about not having done it and releases you to do something you really enjoy.

If you really are struggling, then tell yourself that you are going to do whatever it is for five minutes only. When five minutes is up, you have a choice: you can go and make a drink or stare at your phone and then see if you can do it for another five minutes only. Give it a go!

Plan to succeed this term

Usually your teachers set homework at the same time every week, giving you plenty of time to finish before your deadline – but how often do you leave all your homework to the last minute? If you use this planner, it will help you plan more effectively, meaning you work for a reasonable time every evening, not for five hours on a Thursday night!

Subject:					
Homework set:					
Deadline:					
Mon					
Tues					
Wed					
Thur					
Fri					
Sat					
Sun					
Mon					
Tues					
Wed					
Thur					
Fri					
Sat					
Sun					

Subject:					
Homework set:					
Deadline:					
Mon					
Tues					
Wed					
Thur					
Fri					
Sat					
Sun					
Mon					
Tues					
Wed					
Thur					
Fri					
Sat					
Sun					

Where can you go when you've slammed that door and shouted at your whole family? You need somewhere calm that will soothe you, so you can begin to think clearly again. This can be difficult if you share a bedroom but not impossible. It doesn't even have to be your bedroom; it could be an unused corner of the house or even a shed, as long as you can expect to be alone for the time you need.

- Use cushions or blankets to make your spot cosy.
- If you can, create the feeling of a den by hanging a sheet or blanket over the backs of chairs around you.
- Use warm lighting. Many shops have battery-operated candles, which are excellent for creating a warm glow; please don't use real candles!
- Pack an emergency comfort bag, box or basket. This can contain many objects that relax you but a smartphone is not a good idea. This invites the world in when you need to shut the world out for a few minutes! Instead, include items such as:
    - A favourite book or magazine
    - A fidget toy to fiddle your frustrations away!
    - A loved ornament or toy

You are somebody's reason to smile.

CHAPTER THREE

Everyone could do with tips for making new friends as you travel through life. But it's always important to appreciate those who are lucky enough to be in your life already!

Where would you like to visit or perhaps live one day? There is an exciting world out there and this chapter highlights some of the awesome experiences and opportunities available to you.

MY MATES

Making friends in school can be stressful and tricky. Here are some ways to help you connect with others:

- Keep in mind certain social rules and cues such as not standing too close to someone. Remember to listen to what they say and show interest – don't do all the talking!

- Understand there are different types of friends. Not everybody can be a friend for all situations – and that's OK. For instance, some aren't good at keeping secrets, but they're lots of fun. Some are easy to talk to about feelings, but don't share the same interests. Just because someone isn't "best friend" material, that doesn't mean they can't be a friend at all. It just means there are limitations to that particular friendship.

- Exploring what you have to offer as a friend can also help. Consider what qualities or things make you a good friend to have!

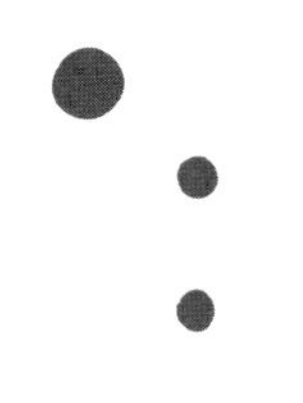

- Sometimes you may not recognize someone as a potential friend; perhaps you have made a snap judgement before noticing that they have the same interests or values.
- On the other hand, you may aim to be friends with someone because they are "popular" despite them having very different values. Think about what values are not negotiable for you – honesty, for example.
- Finally, you need to know how to avoid hurting a friendship. Friends need space and you can't always be together. They may have other friends they want to see sometimes. You and your friend both need a chance to talk about your feelings and what's important to you; and friends can disagree without hurting each other.

Be yourself.
An original
is always
worth more
than a copy.

Suzy Kassem

COOL THREADS

Trying to upgrade your style? Tired of wearing the same old clothes that you've had for years? As you get older you may find yourself more interested in fashion. Developing your own look takes time and energy, but by understanding your body type and current trends, you can easily enhance your vibe!

- A great way to start, especially if you don't know much about fashion, is to read blogs and magazines that are devoted to style and take tips from them.
- Look at celebrities that you like for style cues. Pick a celebrity you admire who has a similar body type and see what clothes you already own that fit the bill.
- A great way to start is to search "boys' style tips" and see what is trending. Then look at your current wardrobe and see if you can emulate popular styles.
- Don't change who you are just for the sake of being on trend or trying to fit in with what's popular. Changing to a certain look or style just because it's *the cool thing to do* doesn't mean it's right for you. More than anything else, be yourself.
- Don't buy into everything you read. While there are trends in fashion, it is largely subjective.
- Keeping up with the latest trends needn't be expensive. Look to second-hand and vintage stores and pre-loved sites for some amazing pieces that you will not find anywhere else.
- How clothes fit on you plays a big role into looking good. Just because you love a particular item doesn't mean it will always suit your body type.

WOULD YOU RATHER...?

Have fun discussing these tantalizing choices with your mates!

Go to school with no trousers for a day
Go to school dressed as a clown for a month

★

Burp every time your parent talks to you
Fart every time a teacher talks to you

★

Spend a night with friends in a haunted house
Spend the night on your own in the woods

★

Be Spiderman for a day
Be the Green Goblin for a day

★

Always enter rooms by announcing your name
Always do cartwheels when leaving a room

★

Not be allowed to watch TV for a year
Not be allowed to eat sweets for a year

★

Never eat pizza again
Only eat pizza

★

Always be dressed for a party
Always wear your pyjamas

★

Live where it is always dark outside but warm
Live where it is always light outside but cold

Be the fastest person in the world
Be able to freeze time

Live a hundred years in the past
Live a hundred years in the future

★

Be the worst player on a team that always wins
Be the best player on a team that always loses

Jump as far as a kangaroo
Hold your breath as long as a whale

Randomly turn into a frog for a day once a month
Randomly turn into a bird for a day once a week

Be the author of a popular book
Be a musician in a popular band

Sing in front of 50 people
Have 1,000 people sing to you

Never have any homework to do
Be paid £10 an hour for doing your homework

Have eyes that change colour depending on your mood
Have hair that changes colour depending on the temperature

Have a house with trampoline floors
Have a house with aquarium walls

Be rich and unknown
Be famous and poor

What a carry on!

Now you're packing your own carry-on luggage for long car journeys and flights, here are the basics for you; you can fill in the rest!

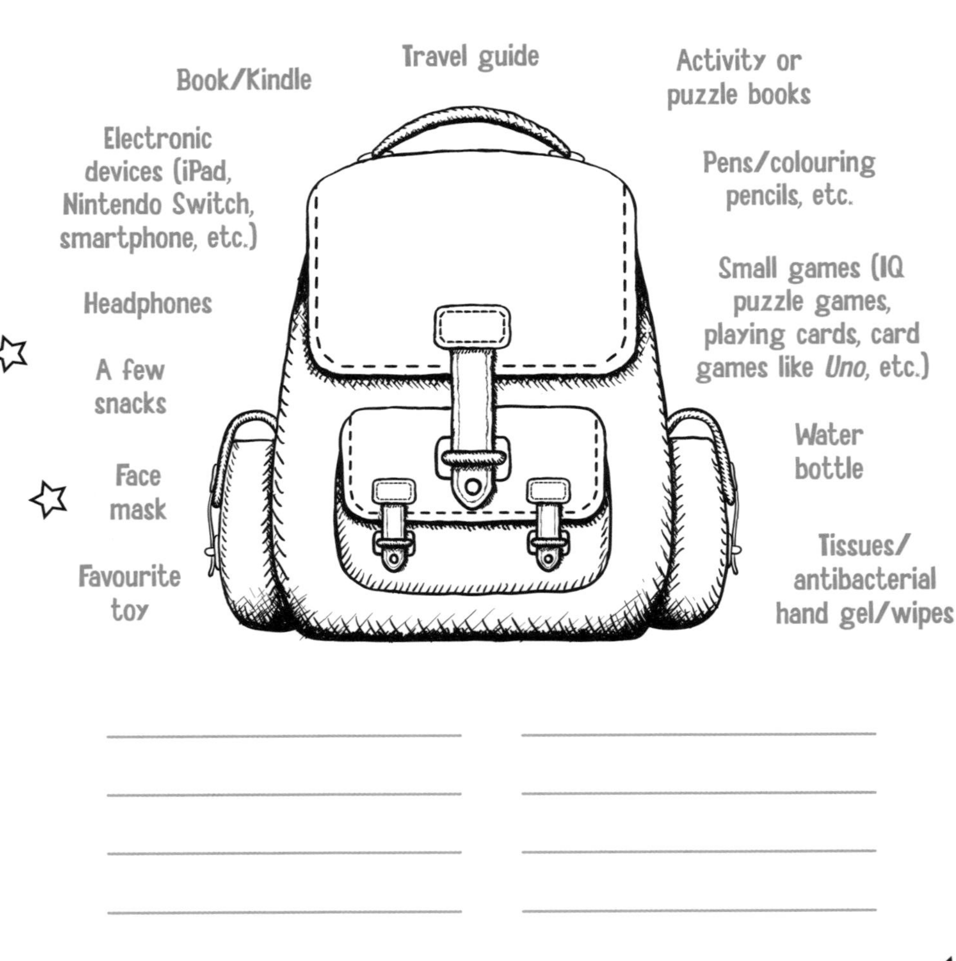

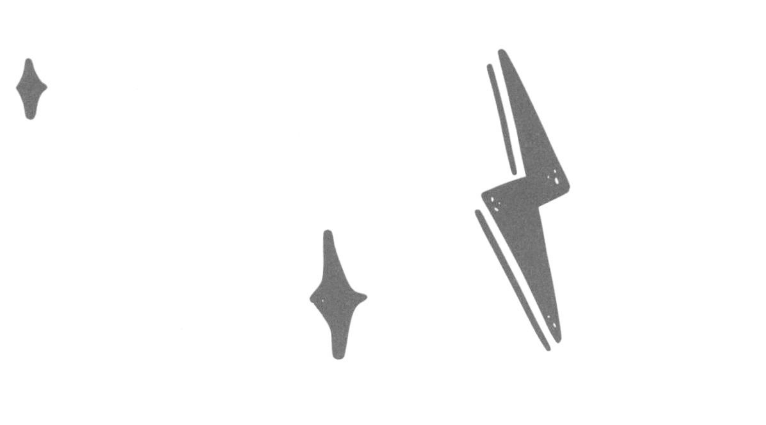

Do things
for joy
or
for learning,
not for
attention.

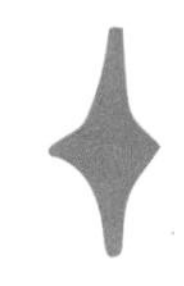
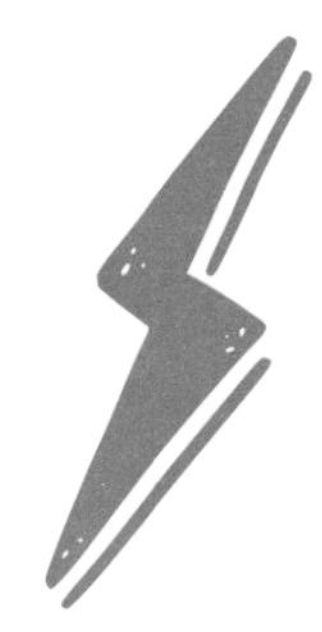

Where in the world?

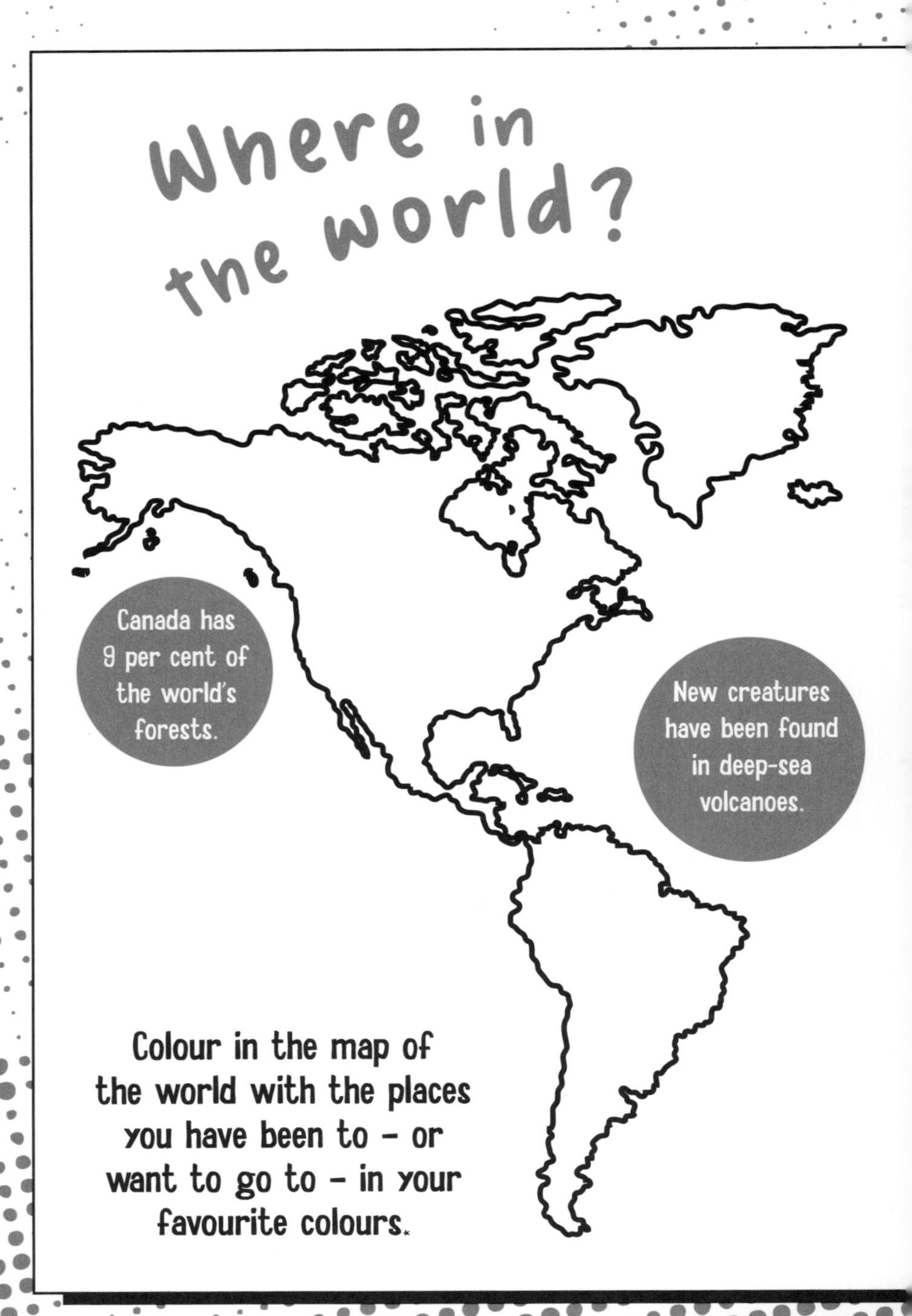

Colour in the map of the world with the places you have been to – or want to go to – in your favourite colours.

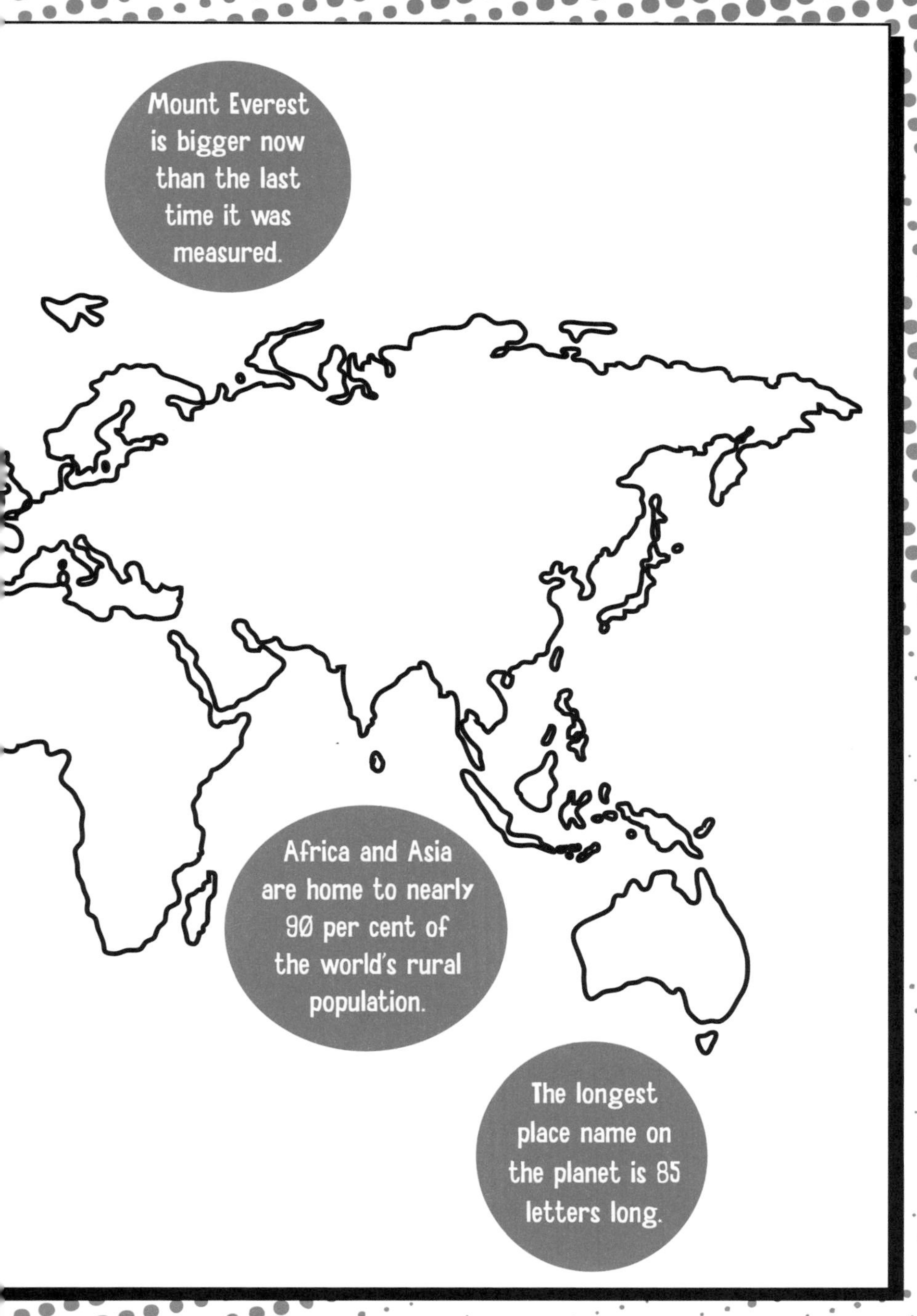
Mount Everest is bigger now than the last time it was measured.
Africa and Asia are home to nearly 90 per cent of the world's rural population.
The longest place name on the planet is 85 letters long.

The Grand Tour

The "Grand Tour" was the seventeenth- and eighteenth-century custom of travelling through Europe, undertaken by British nobility and wealthy landed gentry when they had come of age, at around 21.

This Grand Tour was popular from 1660 until the introduction of commercial rail transport in the 1840s and was viewed as an educational rite of passage.

It was very much based in Europe, but we are giving you the world!

Rank the parts of the world or specific places that you would love to visit from No.1 through to 10, referencing the world map on the previous page.

1) ______

2) ______

3) ______

4) ______

5) ______

6) ______

7) ______

8) ______

9) ______

10) ______

DINING WITH THE STARS!

If you could have anyone from the past or present to your house for supper, who would you invite? What would you give them to eat?

Menu

Starter

Main

Dessert

Are you a city slicker or a country lover?

The countryside (muck-spreading, silage) smells worse than the city (diesel fumes and fast food).

- [ ] a) Strongly Agree
- [ ] b) Agree
- [ ] c) Not sure
- [ ] d) Disagree
- [ ] e) Strongly disagree

I would rather ride a skateboard than a horse.

- [ ] a) Strongly Agree
- [ ] b) Agree
- [ ] c) Not sure
- [ ] d) Disagree
- [ ] e) Strongly disagree

It's a beautiful morning. Do you ...

- [ ] a) Strongly Agree
- [ ] b) Agree
- [ ] c) Even care?
- [ ] d) Disagree
- [ ] e) Strongly disagree

I hardly ever look at the weather forecast.

☐ a) Strongly Agree ☐ b) Agree ☐ c) Not sure

☐ d) Disagree ☐ e) Strongly disagree

I've never bought clothes from a shop that also sells pet food.

☐ a) Strongly Agree ☐ b) Agree ☐ c) Not sure

☐ d) Disagree ☐ e) Strongly disagree

I don't own a pair of wellies that fit me.

☐ a) Strongly Agree ☐ b) Agree ☐ c) Not sure

☐ d) Disagree ☐ e) Strongly disagree

Mostly a) and b) with a scattering of c): Your heart belongs in the city, with the pavement beneath your feet and the sky being something you catch sight of between buildings. The countryside is simply the brown bit you see from the car or train window between towns.

Mostly d) and e) with a smattering of c): Get that straw out of your mouth and ease those wellies off! You are a country boy at heart where nothing smells as sweet as silage and nothing raises your spirits more than birdsong.

Dream Destination Dining

Travel to your favourite place without even leaving your house. Plan an evening with your family and/or friends with food from that country and get everyone to dress up like locals!

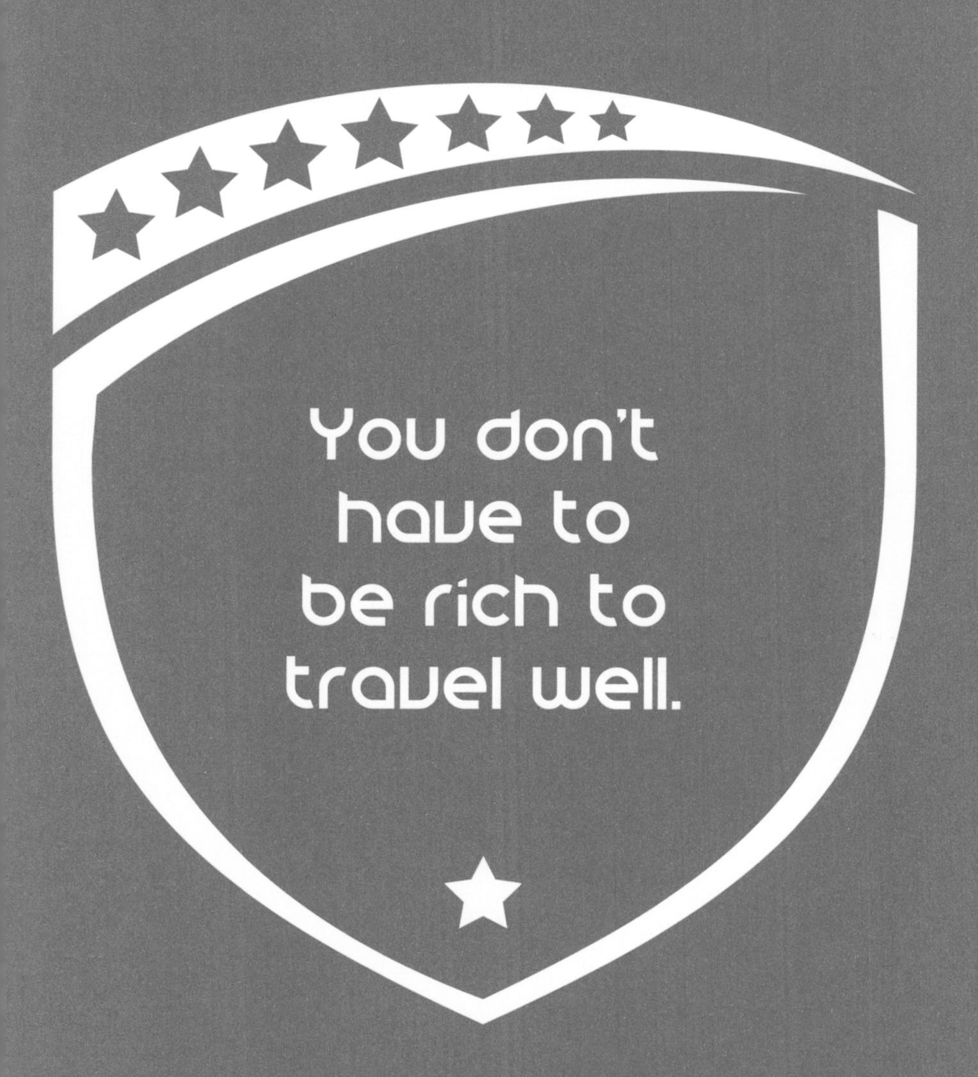

EUGENE FODOR

Party smarty!

A lot of the fun of a party can be in the initial planning and making the guest list with your friends. But there are also less interesting decisions to make and if you don't sort them, they can make the difference between the uber-party of the decade and a political party!

- Ask an older sibling or friend to be there. This will help you relax and enjoy being the host.
- Decide what food and drinks you would like at your party. Don't forget the decorations and activities, too!
- If you are having a smaller party, your house is likely to be a suitable venue; but if you are planning a larger party, consider renting a place such as a local hall – with your parents' help!
- How many friends can you comfortably invite? Come to a compromise with your parents so that both of you have a say in it.
- Agree a soft end time and a firm end time with your parents. The soft end time is when you are expected to start turning off the music and letting everyone know that the party is almost at an end. The firm end time is when the party must be completely over.

- Plan the party for the beginning of the weekend or the holidays so that your guests don't have to worry about getting up the next day.
- Also, find out whether anyone else at your school is having parties around the same time to try to avoid clashes!
- Be sure to let your neighbours know about the party in advance. This will make them more forgiving of the noise.

- Provide large, clearly labelled waste and recycling bins. The fewer excuses your friends have to be messy, the better.
- If you don't want party-goers entering certain rooms, lock them. It is also a good idea to lock away anything valuable.
- Set up a music system. All you'll need for this are decent speakers and a smartphone/tablet/mp3 hook-up. Don't try to DJ for the party the whole night – it's fun to share the music!
- Recruit close friends for the clean-up the next day. Make it fun with music and the leftover food (or maybe order a pizza in)!

Keep your parents in the loop with all of the arrangements. The more you show them that you can be responsible and that you've considered all the aspects of your party, the likelier it will be that they will give you more responsibility and more parties!

TAKE A SHOT!

You don't have to travel far to find the best travel photography tips.

- You don't need all the gear. Taking that *perfect* shot is all about the right subject and the right atmosphere. A good old smartphone will do the trick – they're much easier to carry around and the settings are simpler to use than on a camera. You could even buy a waterproof cover for underwater pictures or action shots while white-water rafting and kayaking!

- It doesn't have to be what everyone else is staring at. If you see something that looks interesting and exciting to you, take a picture. It might not be a direct shot of the Taj Mahal: what about someone's expression on first seeing the Taj Mahal – who else will have that shot?

- To capture stunning photos of local people, practise at home.
- Before you head off on holiday, start practising by taking pictures of something you love at home – something that really interests you.

- Try different angles. Look at your subject from the left, right or even upside down. Get up high or crouch low. This will give you some totally unique photos.
- Don't delete anything! Probably the tip to remember. Resist the temptation to scroll through your pics at the end of each day, deleting something that's a little out of focus or didn't come out as planned. You never know – your image might look better bigger, in a different colour or cropped, or you might just feel completely different about it when you get home.

- See with your eyes, not the lens. Remember to put the camera down and take a good look at what interests you before you start snapping away.

- It's not just the places, but the people who make your image too. Although travelling to far-flung places is always amazing, our memories wouldn't be half as brilliant if we didn't go with our families and friends. Don't forget to capture photos of you all having fun together, as well as the incredible scenery and wildlife around you.

Not-to-be-missed list

It's never too early to make plans for the future-fabulous you!

TRIP	DATE PLANNED	NAME OF TRAVEL BUDDY	DONE
1) Plan one trip alone. Few things are as exciting or liberating as travelling on your own.			
2) Go on an African safari.			
3) Have a gelato in St Mark's Square in Venice, Italy.			
4) Backpack around Europe.			
5) Play cricket in the street in India.			
6) Volunteer abroad.			
7) Visit Uluru-Kata Tjuta National Park in central Australia.			

8) Walk along the Great Wall of China.			
9) Take a road trip coast to coast in the USA.			
10) Camel trek among the Pyramids in Giza, Egypt.			
11) Stay in the Lake Palace in Udaipur, India.			
12) Learn to scuba dive.			
13) Take a river cruise past story-book castles on the Rhine, Germany.			
14) Take the Trans-Siberian Express from Moscow to Vladivostok, Russia.			
15) Be a space tourist and stay in the world's first space hotel.			

STRENGTH

is a power of

THE MIND,

not the body.

BAG IT!

Be honest: do you wrap your presents for your friends and family or do you get someone else to do it for you?

Well, no more! This is an awesome hack for making gift bags that look impressive and will immediately make any item inside them seem desirable.

You will need a cardboard box, or anything of a similar shape, such as a thick book, wooden block, etc. Just make sure it's big enough for your gift to fit inside. Now it's the perfect opportunity to reuse some wrapping paper!

1) Take a piece of wrapping paper long enough to wrap around the box, or join two pieces together with tape.

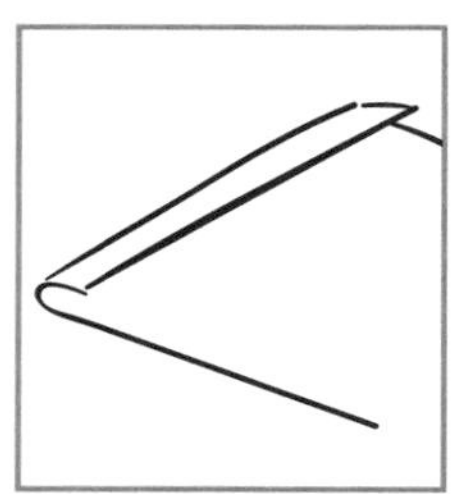

2) Fold the top edge for a clean look, and to provide more support for the handles.

3) Wrap the paper around the box, tape at the end, and press along the four sides so the edges are more defined.

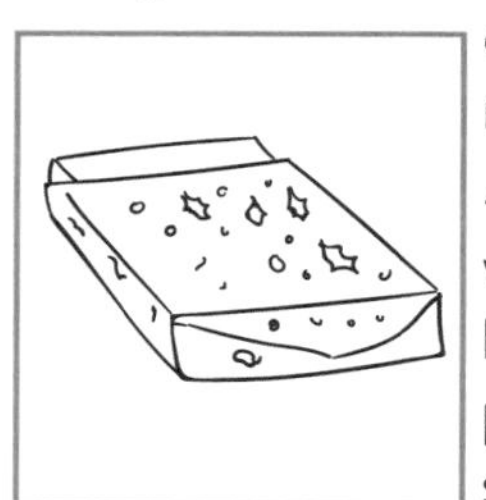

4) Fold and wrap the bottom portion in the same way you would wrap a gift box, then secure with clear tape.

5) Slide the "gift bag" from the box.

6) The handles can be made out of ribbons, paper, rope or even scrap fabrics. You can twist two pieces of tissue paper into a paper rope and glue them onto the bag. Or with ribbons, just punch a couple of holes on each side of the bag and thread the ribbons through, tying a knot on the inside to hold them in place.

CHAPTER FOUR

There is no one quite like you and never will be again because you are unique! This chapter will show you what this means and how you can make a real difference to the world around you.

Social skills

Have a think about the important social skills listed on this page and write an intention under each one. For example, you could write that the next time you have some chocolate, you will share it with your little brother!

Sharing

Cooperating

Listening

Following directions

Respecting personal space

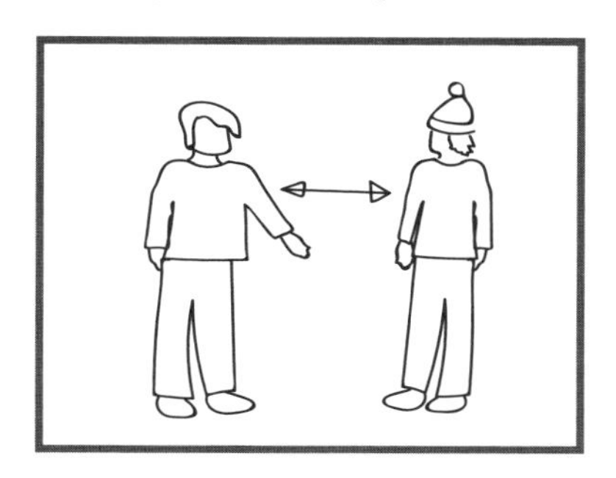

Making eye contact

Using manners

PLEASE

THANK YOU

Success is no accident.
It is hard work, perseverance,
learning, studying, sacrifice
and most of all, love
of what you are doing
or learning to do.

Pelé

Gender identity is your sense of who you are – male, female, both or neither. It sounds simple but can get very confusing, so this is our straightforward guide for you.

You might identify as cisgender. This is when your gender identity is male or female, and it's the same as the sex you were at birth.

Or you might identify as gender diverse, which includes:

- Transgender – your gender identity doesn't match the sex given at birth.
- Non-binary – your gender identity is neither male nor female, or it's a blend of male and female.
- Gender fluid – you move between gender identities.
- Agender – you don't identify with any gender.

Or you might use another term to identify gender. And you might discover or understand more about your gender identity over time. This might mean you express your identity in new or different ways.

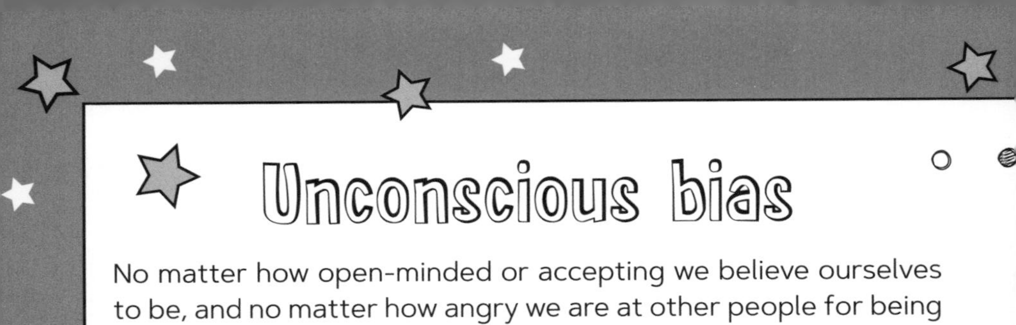

Unconscious bias

No matter how open-minded or accepting we believe ourselves to be, and no matter how angry we are at other people for being mean and hateful because someone is thought to be different, the fact remains: we all carry prejudice and biases.

Use these journal prompts to explore your experiences with – and attitudes about – difference.

1) The first time I became aware of differences was when...

____

____

____

2) My parents, teachers and carers have taught me that people who are different from us are...

____

____

____

3) My parents, teachers and carers taught me that people who are like us are...

____

____

____

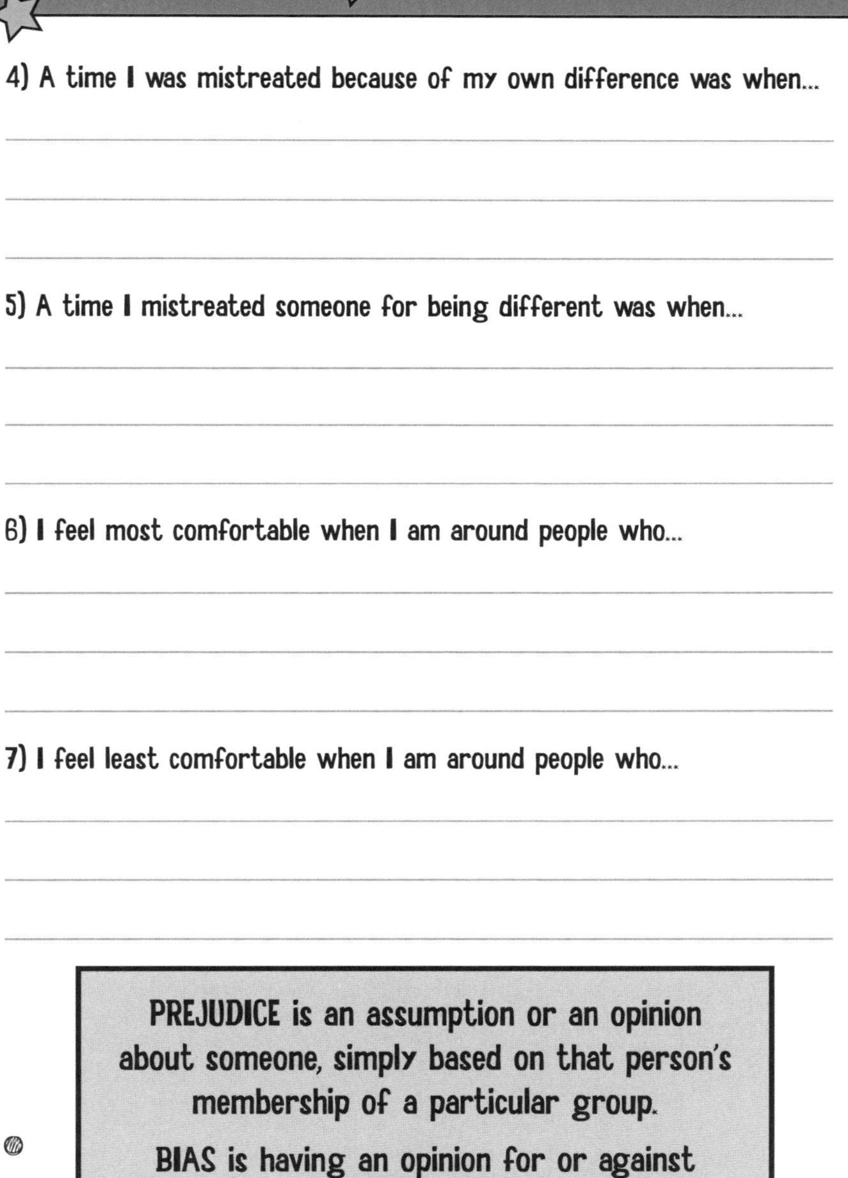

4) A time I was mistreated because of my own difference was when...

5) A time I mistreated someone for being different was when...

6) I feel most comfortable when I am around people who...

7) I feel least comfortable when I am around people who...

PREJUDICE is an assumption or an opinion about someone, simply based on that person's membership of a particular group.

BIAS is having an opinion for or against one person or group, especially in a way considered to be unfair.

Find your voice!

Knowing how to write a good letter is a very useful skill. It comes in handy when you want to persuade someone to understand your point of view. Whether you're emailing your teacher or writing a letter for a school project, a great letter will help you get your message across and ensure you are heard.

Include the following in every letter you write, and you will get results:

- Your name and address at the top right-hand corner.
- Your recipient's address lower down on the left.
- The date under your name and address.
- The greeting should be Dear Mr/Mrs/Ms/Dr, etc. and their surname; or, if you don't know it, Dear Sir/Madam
- A short introductory sentence, giving the reason why you're writing.
- The body of the letter should provide evidence that supports your position: be persuasive!
- The closing paragraph should sum up your argument.
- Always close with "Yours sincerely", if you greeted them by name at the top of the letter, or "Yours faithfully" if you wrote Dear Sir/Madam. These closing words should be on separate line below the letter.

Don't forget your signature at the bottom!

Mistakes
are proof
that you
are trying.

JOIN UP!

We all know it's important to get involved with our communities and treat those who are less fortunate than us with compassion, not judgement, so discover the value of volunteering with one or more of these ideas:

- Walk around your neighbourhood with a bag and pick up rubbish – ask a grown-up or older sibling to accompany you.
- Offer to help a neighbour with small gardening jobs, like raking leaves.
- Offer to fundraise for a local issue, such as new playground equipment.
- Find out if you have any elderly neighbours who have any jobs with which you are able to help.
- Bring smiles to the elderly in your community by visiting or volunteering at a local care home.
- Get involved with a local park or beach clean-up.
- Join local groups that offer built-in volunteer opportunities, such as the Scouts or Guides.
- Organize a food bank collection at school.
- Sort out any old toys, games and clothes and give them to your local charity shops.
- Discover local events, such as 5K or fun runs, or other events that donate proceeds to local charities helping those in need.
- Ask about volunteering opportunities in your community.
- Donate newspapers or other much-needed pet supplies to a local animal shelter.

Whether it's volunteering for your neighbours, for local charities, with animals, or joining local social or activist groups, there are multiple ways to donate your time and talents to help others in your community or nationwide. Have a chat with your friends and decide on four ways you could make a difference over the coming year. Write your ideas here:

1) ____________________

____

____

____

2) ____________________

____

____

____

3) ____________________

____

____

____

4) ____________________

____

____

____

Don't care!

Here are some ways to stop worrying about what other people think.

Keep things in perspective

It's said that people would care a lot less about what others think about them if they knew how *little* others think about them. And it's true! Everyone has enough to occupy their mind. They also have their own insecurities. If you're worried about how you come across to someone you've just met, keep in mind that they're probably doing the same.

Question your thinking

Sometimes we assume the worst, or filter out the good in a situation and only notice the bad. Pay attention to your thoughts and question them, rather than allowing perhaps false impressions to become real. You may discover that what you're fretting over exists only in your mind.

Let go of perfection

It can be hard to shake the feeling that if you just get things right you will never have any problems again with friends etc. and everything in life will fall into place. But this just isn't true, not only because no one can ever achieve true perfection, but because what people think about you has more to do with *them* than with you.

Get to know yourself

What do you really like? What do you really want? Are you making choices about your friendships and interests because you want them or because they'll please or impress someone else? Allow yourself to try new things and wonder, "What would I try or enjoy if I wasn't so worried about what other people think?"

Find your tribe

Somewhere out there are people who have the same interests as you and will appreciate you just as you are. Don't waste time trying to be like others; just be yourself.

Allow yourself to step out of your comfort zone

It can be terrifying to go against the "crowd", speak out, take a risk or face disapproval. But decide what matters to you, trust yourself and go for it. We don't grow by always playing it safe; we grow by allowing ourselves a chance to fail.

Accept a helping hand

The worry you feel about what others think can sometimes be overcome with a little self-awareness. Other times, try to talk to a trusted adult, as talking about these types of worries often helps.

Be your own best friend

It's important to understand that you will never be able to make everyone like you, no matter what you do. But look on the bright side: no one else can do it, either. So accept the twinges that will inevitably come when you realize you haven't made a connection with someone, and focus instead on a goal that will take you further toward being the kind of person you want to be – learning to like yourself, flaws and all.

What kind of Eco-Warrior are you?

You've just finished playing sport and your bottle of water. What's your next move?

a) Save the bottle top for a future project.

b) Fill it up again and put it in the fridge, making a mental note to ask your parents for a reusable water bottle.

c) Put it in the recycling box.

d) Cut off its bottom and use it to protect new plants.

Your gran knitted you a striped yellow and purple jumper for Christmas. You couldn't possibly wear it, so what are you going to do?

a) Unravel the wool to knit scarves for Christmas presents next year!

b) Cut off the arms, fill them with old tights and socks and make a draught excluder.

c) Put it on a hot wash and shrink it to make teddy clothes for a younger sibling.

d) Wear it to work in the garden or the allotment.

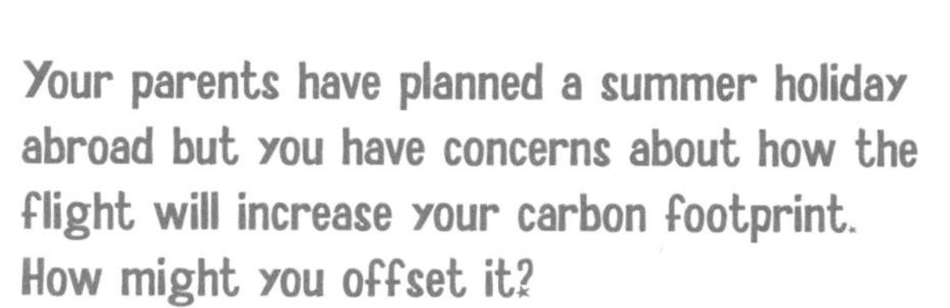

Your parents have planned a summer holiday abroad but you have concerns about how the flight will increase your carbon footprint. How might you offset it?

a) Instead of buying new holiday gear, upcycle some of last year's.

b) Encourage your parents to hire bikes where they can, reducing carbon emissions while away.

c) Find out where the nearest recycling facilities are and how the locals approach recycling.

d) Install a water butt in the garden so you can water your veggies with rainwater when you return.

Your three mucky brothers and sisters have used up a lot of water getting themselves clean. What do you do to offset the water use?

a) Create a patchwork bath towel from old flannels.

b) Postpone your shower to another day. You don't smell *that* much.

c) Make a toy submarine from plastic bottles instead of buying them one.

d) Fill up the watering can for the garden with the dirty bath water. The plants don't seem to mind!

Your parents are complaining about the latest electricity bill. What are you going to do to help out?

a) Trawl charity shops for old blankets to curl up under on the sofa so you don't have to turn up the heating.

b) Make sure all electrical appliances are unplugged when you go to bed.

c) Join a book-swap club so you don't spend all evening watching TV or playing computer games.

d) If you can grow some vegetables and herbs, you can use the money you save on shopping to go toward paying the bill!

Your kitchen cupboard is full to the brim with plastic bags. What do you plan to do with them?

a) Take them to the recycling centre.

b) Use them to fill in any holes in brickwork or draughty areas and keep the warmth in.

c) Put them in the car and make sure they are reused.

d) Tie them around your knees when you're gardening so your legs don't get dirty.

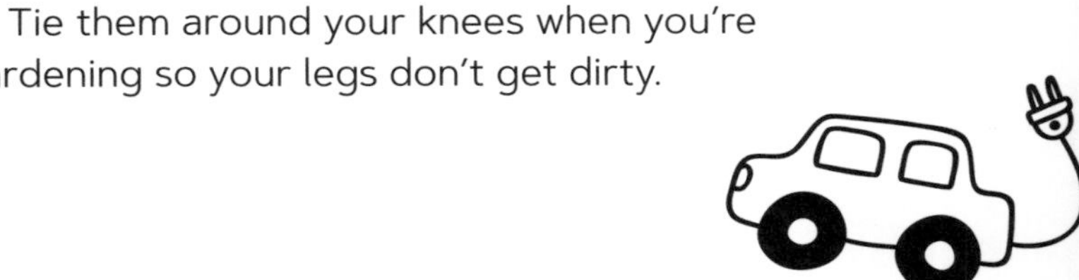

If you answered mostly a) you're a Cool Crafter!

In your house, nothing goes to waste: you're very creative and always have lots of projects on the go. Everyone wants to get a gift from you!

If you answered mostly b) you're an Energy Saviour!

No appliance is ever left on standby in your house and you'd rather put on another jumper than turn the thermostat up a degree. Evenings are spent turning off lights, draught-proofing and persuading your parents to buy some solar panels for the roof.

If you answered mostly c) you're a Waste Warrior!

You know exactly when to put out the recycling and you won't let your mum put anything in the bin that can't be washed and recycled. Your school lunches are packed in reusable boxes, and you've already started on this year's Christmas cards – made from last year's!

If you answered mostly d) you're a Gardening Guru!

You love nothing more than sowing next year's seeds and harvesting your latest crop of fruit and veg. You're constantly pestering your mum for food scraps to turn into compost and will happily show off your brand new wormery.

Just as you notice the behaviour of those around you, it's fascinating to check in with yourself sometimes. Often you judge others without realizing you are doing the same thing yourself!

Think about five situations in the last month where you behaved in a way that perhaps you wouldn't do now, having thought about it. Here's an example:

I carried on playing football with a few of my friends after I had noticed one of my other friends walking around on his own. Now I'm thinking I would have liked to have asked him if anything was wrong, making him feel cared for.

1) ______________________________

____

2) ______________________________

____

3) ______________________________

____

4) ______________________________

____

5) ______________________________

____

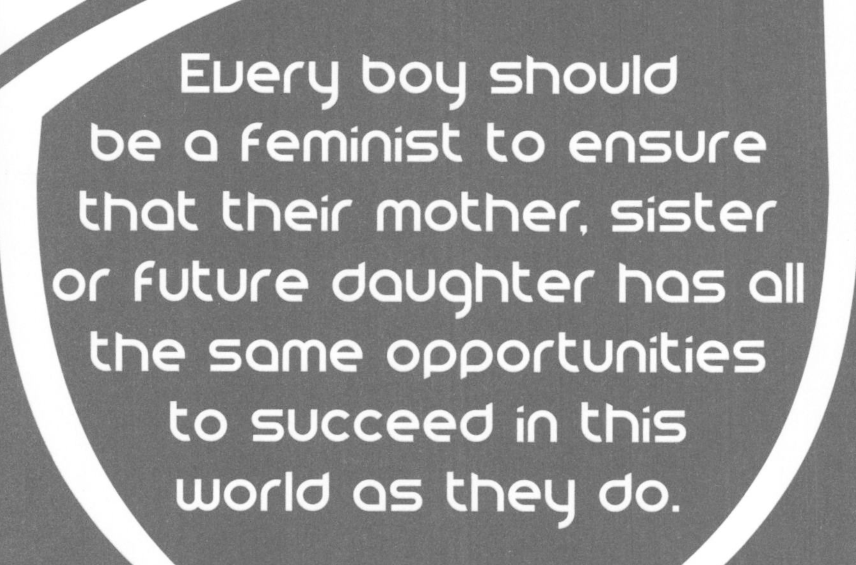

EITAN BERNATH

Boys are feminists too!

Feminism means believing in equal rights for both boys and girls in society. What boy wouldn't believe that? Many people misunderstand the term feminism so we are going to dispel some of the myths and mistruths that you can find widely on the internet. These myths are:

- Women are too sensitive
- Women seek special privileges.
- We've already reached equality so it's unnecessary.

If you believe that boys and girls, and then women and men, should experience the same rights and attitudes in society, then two of the above statements are not relevant, because it's important to realize that:

- Men and women can both be sensitive or not.
- Women only seek privileges that men enjoy too.

Unfortunately, most of you will know that, as a society, we haven't reached equality between the sexes in politics, the judicial system or the public sector (police, hospitals, schools, etc.).

But you can be the agent we need for change, making true equality everybody's experience across the world.

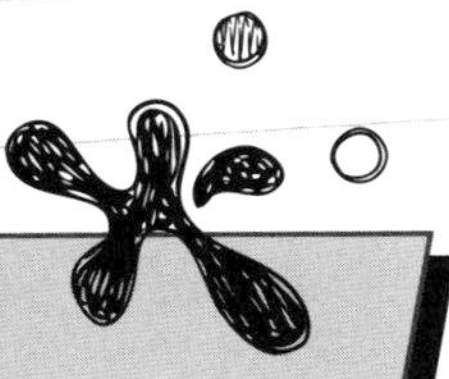

THINGS TO REMEMBER:

- Understand that gender equality is not a woman's problem; it is a human problem. We are all humans and we all believe we should be treated equally.
- Your masculinity will not be threatened by supporting women's rights. It's a common misconception that when women are elevated, it means men are brought down. That couldn't be further from the truth – it means that we are all lifted together.
- Imagine what can be accomplished when half of the world's population isn't held back by prejudice. Not only will this have a major socio-economic impact but there will be tremendous breakthroughs in every field of work that ultimately will advance humankind.
- Think when searching online – there are millions of opinions on the internet and you need to understand that just because it's written down in front of you, that doesn't make it true!
- Recognize any gender stereotypes (oversimplified images or ideas of a particular type of person or thing) and be prepared to challenge them.

No means NO!

Boys can often get the idea (wrongly) that saying no is weak. This can make it hard for them to object if a friend goes too far and hard for them to accept a "no" from others. True strength is saying what you really mean. Someone who knows they can say no if they don't want to do something is more likely to respect a "no" from other people.

You should have discussed consent at school or with your family. These questions are to check that you thoroughly understand that no one can make you do anything physically that you haven't clearly agreed to.

1) If someone gives you a present, it means you have to do what they want.

☐ True ☐ False

2) You can borrow your friend's jacket without asking them first.

☐ True ☐ False

3) If someone is wearing a swimming costume, you can force them to go swimming.

☐ True ☐ False

4) If someone invites you to their house, it's OK for them to force you to do exactly what they want.

☐ True ☐ False

5) If someone has had too many sweets at a party and is feeling very sick and wants to lie down, it's OK for you to force them to get up and dance.

☐ True ☐ False

6) If you hate being tickled and have told people you hate being tickled, it's OK for someone to ignore that and tickle you anyway.

☐ True ☐ False

7) If you offer someone a hot chocolate and they change their minds, having said yes at first, it's OK for you to force them to drink it.

☐ True ☐ False

If you answered "true" for any of these statements, then it's important that you talk to your parents or teachers about consent.

Be a good ally!

It's never too early to start the conversation about race. Hundreds of years after the end of slavery and decades after race equality, racism still exists. It's so important to educate ourselves about race and allyship, with the goal of creating a better world for us all. It won't happen overnight, but if we continue to call for justice wherever injustice strikes and educate ourselves, we will be much closer. The following books are the best place to start but there are many more, so please add them below when you've read them!

Noughts and Crosses
by Malorie Blackman

This Book Is Anti-Racist
by Tiffany Jewell and Aurélia Durand

The Undefeated
by Kwame Alexander and Kadir Nelson

All American Boys
by Jason Reynolds and Brendan Kiely

Piecing Me Together
by Renée Watson

____

____

____

Have a think about what makes a good ally...

- Allies spend a lot of time **listening**. When a person from a discriminated group shares their experience, allies listen and try to understand. They make sure their friend feels heard and supported.

- Allies also spend a lot of time **learning**. They seek to learn about the history of discrimination. They also find out about current events and try to learn how to better support the people around them.

- While learning, allies also think about their own experiences and face the **biases** they may have formed. Allies also learn a lot about privilege. This means special advantages based on race, gender, class, ability or other parts of one's identity. Allies learn what kind of privilege they may have and how they can use it to help others.

- Finally, allies **get into good trouble**. They speak up and show up. Allies don't stay quiet when they see others being bullied or treated unfairly.

Have you ever spoken up for a friend or sibling who you felt was being bullied or treated unfairly? Do you know any trusted adults who call themselves allies? To learn more about what that means, talk to them. They'll be able to share what the word means to them and how they act to support others.

BE A SUPPORTER!

Description of charity	Reasons for my support

Research your top six charities, social groups or causes that you would like to support, in any way that you can. Fill these in below and write down what it is about them that earns your support.

What I intend to do for this charity

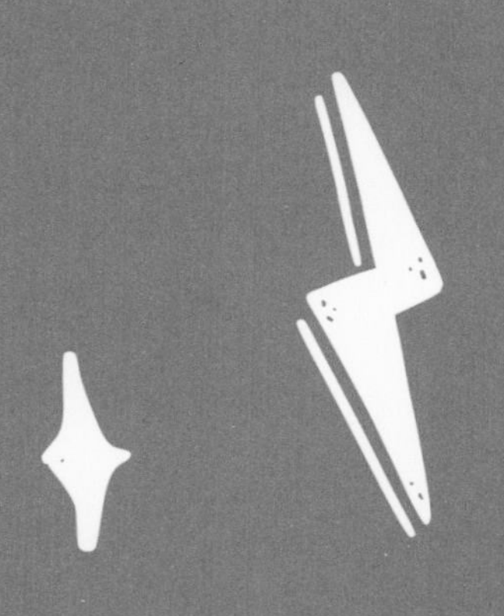

Next to trying
and winning,
the best thing
is trying
and failing.

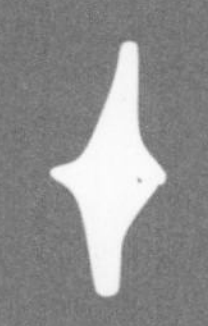

Safer streets

We all need to make sure that we can go about our lives safely, without fear. Boys can actively go out of their way to ensure that girls and women feel safe.

- **Listen.** Listen to the women in your life: your mum, sisters and friends. Ask for their thoughts and act on them.
- **Give space**. Cross the road to avoid walking or running directly behind a woman or girl. Make sure you give them safe space – for example, give them the side of the pavement with the light. When you do pass, accelerate ahead. Also, if you are wearing a hoodie, take it down.
- **Don't stare**. Being stared at is intimidating and unsettling. Taking out your phone and focusing on that keeps you in your own space.
- **Keep your comments to yourself.** Don't try to strike up conversations with girls when they are walking or on public transport. If the carriage or bus is empty, sit at a distance.
- **Call out any harassment**. Talk to other boys, as many can be oblivious. If you witness even low-key harassment, be it banter or teasing, if it isn't acceptable, step in!
- **Walk your friends home**. People are safer in groups than on their own.
- **Respect everyone.** If you do this, then you can feel good knowing that people, no matter what their gender is, will feel safe around you.

CHAPTER FIVE

We all have hopes and dreams
for the future but yours
are different because you are
going to make yours a reality!
The first day of your future
is now and the best place
to begin is this chapter.
Good luck!

Performance practice makes for perfect performance

Learning, practising and mastering the basic skills of sport is one of the foundations of coaching, sports performance and athletic training. However, just learning a sports skill is only the first step in the process. Athletes do not fail because their skill level is poor: they fail because their ability to perform the skill in competition conditions is poor and that's a coaching issue.

Performance practice: train the way you want to perform

1) Perform the **skill.**
2) Perform the **skill very well.**
3) Perform the **skill very well and at speed.**
4) Perform the **skill very well, at speed and under fatigue.**
5) Perform the **skill very well, at speed, under fatigue and under pressure.**
6) Perform the **skill very well, at speed, under fatigue and under pressure consistently.**
7) Perform the **skill very well, at speed, under fatigue and under pressure consistently in competition conditions.**

Every coach, every athlete, every media commentator, and every fan will tell you that the fundamental element of all sports is particular **skills:**

- **Kicking and passing in football**
- **Throwing and catching in cricket and baseball**
- **Diving, turning and finishing in swimming**
- **Passing and shooting in basketball and netball**

Being able to perform the skill under competition conditions *once* could be luck; but being able to do it consistently under competition conditions is the sign of a true champion. Consistency with skills in competition comes from **consistency of training standards.** Adopting a "no-compromise" approach to the quality of skills at training will develop a consistent quality of skills in competition conditions. Unfortunately, many athletes have two brains:

- **Training brain** – the brain they use in training and preparation. This brain accepts laziness, inaccuracy and poor skills, believing that *"it will be OK on the day"* and everything will somehow come together at the competition.
- **Competition brain** – the brain they use in competition.

The secret to competition success is to use your "competition brain" in every session.

This is what it is all about. The real factor in what makes a champion athlete is their capacity to perform consistently in competition conditions.

Performing a basic skill well is not difficult. But add fatigue, monumental pressure, the expectations of the coach, the management, teammates and tens of thousands of fans and that basic skill is suddenly not so basic!

For me, sometimes it's more important to perform well in training and know that I am improving rather than scoring in a game. It's doing the hard work, day in, day out.

Marcus Rashford

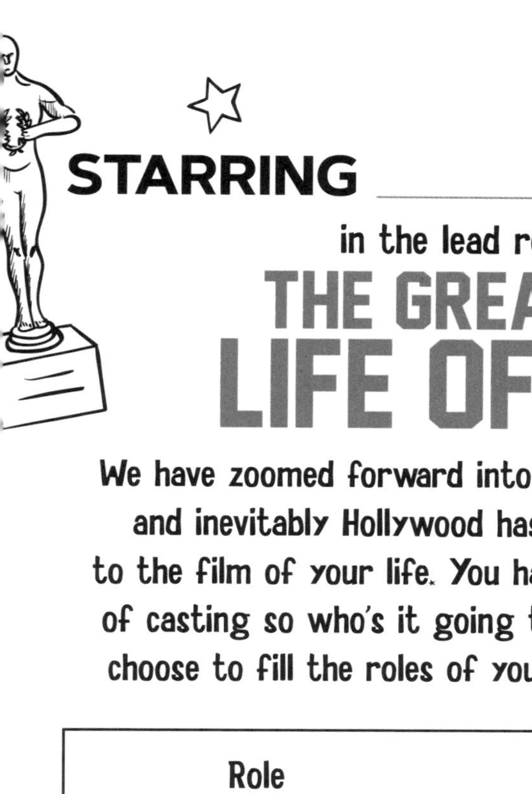

STARRING ______________________________

in the lead role of

THE GREATEST LIFE OF ALL

We have zoomed forward into your awesome future and inevitably Hollywood has bought the rights to the film of your life. You have the ultimate choice of casting so who's it going to be? Who would you choose to fill the roles of your family and friends?

Role	Cast

Jobs Jamboree!

What do you want to be when you "grow up"? If you know, then you're very lucky; lots of people still have no idea when they are well on their way through adulthood! If you are unsure, then these questions may help to steer you toward an exciting career that's perfect for you!

1) If you were an animal, which of these would you be?

- ☐ **a) A chimpanzee**
- ☐ **b) A horse**
- ☐ **c) A kitten**
- ☐ **d) A lion**

2) What area is most likely to be your responsibility in a group project?

- ☐ **a) Drawing illustrations and creating charts.**
- ☐ **b) Presenting the project.**
- ☐ **c) Taking the lead and managing the project.**
- ☐ **d) Background research and providing key facts.**

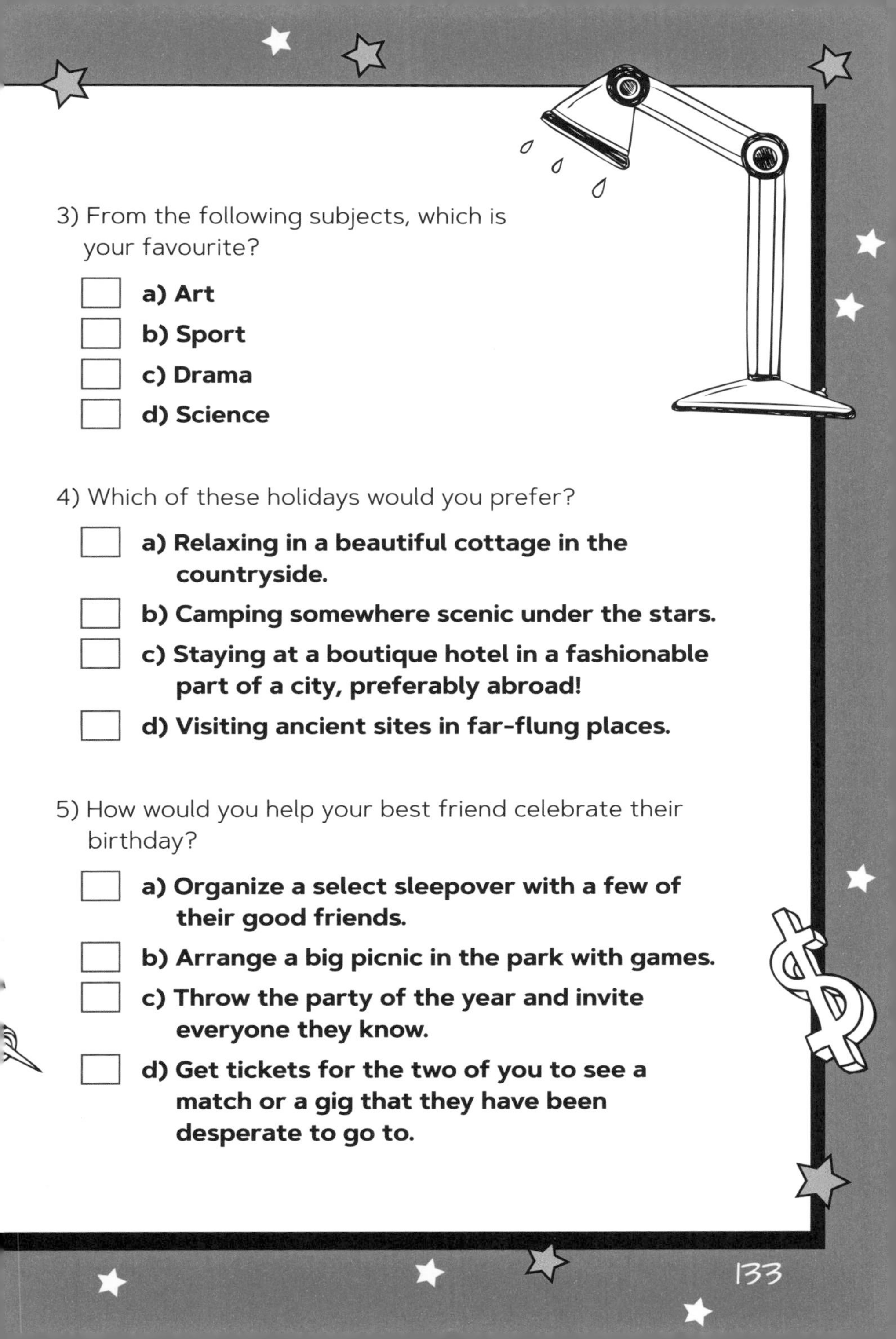

3) From the following subjects, which is your favourite?

- [ ] **a) Art**
- [ ] **b) Sport**
- [ ] **c) Drama**
- [ ] **d) Science**

4) Which of these holidays would you prefer?

- [ ] **a) Relaxing in a beautiful cottage in the countryside.**
- [ ] **b) Camping somewhere scenic under the stars.**
- [ ] **c) Staying at a boutique hotel in a fashionable part of a city, preferably abroad!**
- [ ] **d) Visiting ancient sites in far-flung places.**

5) How would you help your best friend celebrate their birthday?

- [ ] **a) Organize a select sleepover with a few of their good friends.**
- [ ] **b) Arrange a big picnic in the park with games.**
- [ ] **c) Throw the party of the year and invite everyone they know.**
- [ ] **d) Get tickets for the two of you to see a match or a gig that they have been desperate to go to.**

6) Which of the following gifts would mean more to you?

- ☐ **a) A book subscription from your favourite local bookshop.**
- ☐ **b) A trip to the local climbing centre.**
- ☐ **c) A new mobile phone cover.**
- ☐ **d) A trip to a planetarium.**

7) Which of the following would you most like to be awarded?

- ☐ **a) The Nobel Peace Prize**
- ☐ **b) A gold medal at the Olympics**
- ☐ **c) An Oscar**
- ☐ **d) An OBE**

8) Which of the following is the most important to you?

- ☐ **a) Creativity**
- ☐ **b) Freedom**
- ☐ **c) Fame**
- ☐ **d) Success**

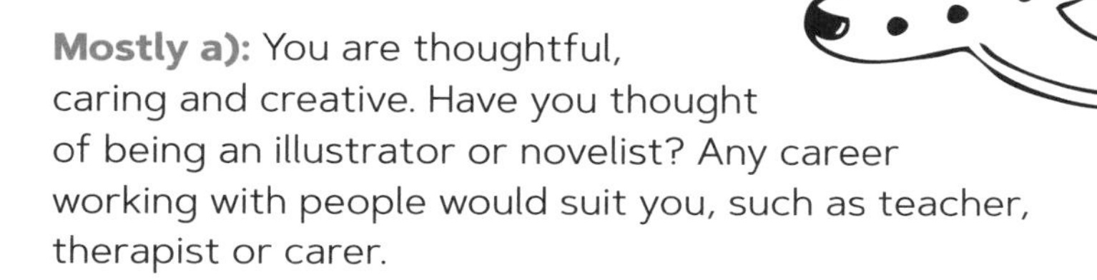

Mostly a): You are thoughtful, caring and creative. Have you thought of being an illustrator or novelist? Any career working with people would suit you, such as teacher, therapist or carer.

Mostly b): You love being physical and outdoors. A nature conservationist would be great or anything in ecology or environmental. You could also consider landscape gardening or journalism.

Mostly c): You are the most likely of these categories to become famous. You love planning events and organizing your friends, so have you thought of public relations? You could also consider the media, TV or radio presenting, acting, etc.

Mostly d): You aren't afraid to study and work hard to make your dreams come true. You are motivated by money and earning respect. Perhaps you should think in the direction of banking, medicine, law or architecture.

Think about those who have had an impact on you during your life so far: they could be people you know or celebrities you want to model yourself on. Write their names in the 12 spaces around the edge of the clock and in the middle, draw a picture of yourself in ten years' time.

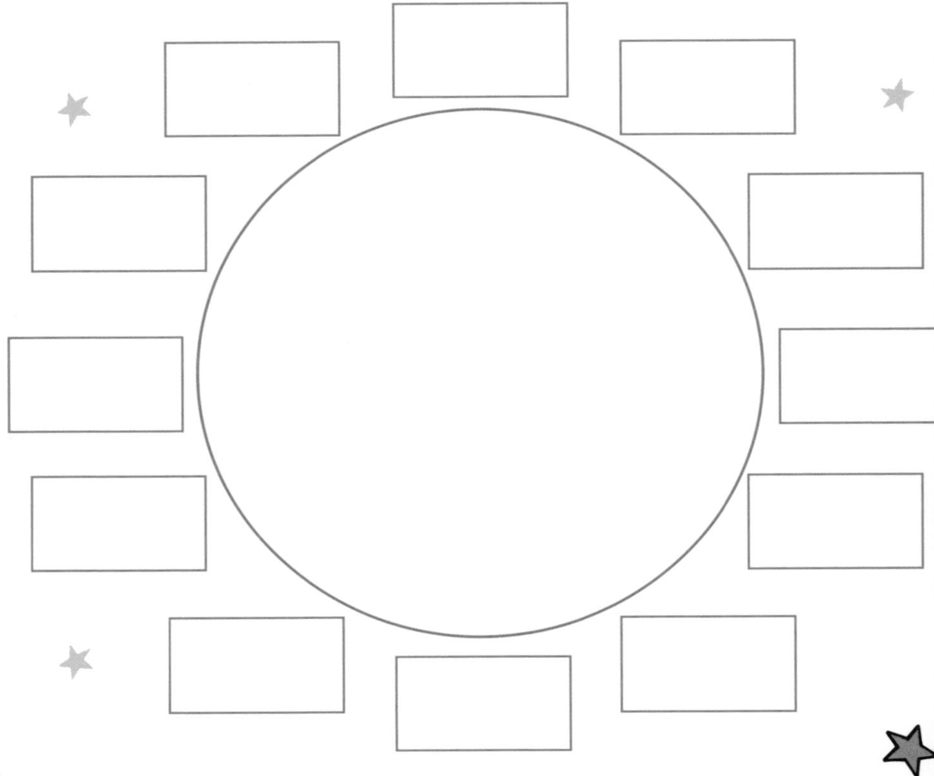

EVERY ACCOMPLISHMENT

starts with the decision

TO TRY.

RESEARCHING THE ROLE

Choose five jobs for which you might be interested in applying in the future.

1) ______________________________

____

2) ______________________________

____

3) ______________________________

____

4) ______________________________

____

5) ______________________________

____

Choose five people, celebrities or people you know, who do these jobs.

1) ______________________________

____

2) ______________________________

____

3) ______________________________

____

4) ______________________________

____

5) ______________________________

____

Research online (or just ask!) how these people got their opportunities. Was there some luck involved in getting the job they wanted? Did they tailor their learning at school toward their goal? Did they write thousands of letters or did they adopt a more targeted approach?

For each job, write down any tips, ideas and facts about how each of these people got to where they wanted to be.

1) ______________________________

2) ______________________________

3) ______________________________

4) ______________________________

5) ______________________________

Sailing to success on the seven Cs

You will have many choices to make as you enter adulthood. Once you decide on a career path, success may depend on how resilient you are. We all know the story of J. K. Rowling, who took 13 attempts before she found a willing publisher, and we know the rest of the story!

Seven Cs for resilience:

Confidence
This comes from believing in yourself.

Competence
This comes from skills you have learned at school, college or from an apprenticeship.

Connection
The ability to form lasting relationships.

Character
Your core values, what makes you tick!

Contribution
Learning the joy of giving, contributing to the world around you.

Coping
Life has its ups and downs, but the key to success is how you spring back from disappointment.

Control
Core to resilience is knowing that your actions matter. Without a sense of control, we cannot possess hope. And without hope, we crumble in challenging times.

MY BEST BITS!

WRITE DOWN THE TEN GREATEST THINGS ABOUT YOU!

1) ______________________________

____

2) ______________________________

____

3) ______________________________

____

4) ______________________________

____

5) ______________________________

____

6) ______________________________

____

7) ______________________________

____

8) ______________________________

____

9) ______________________________

____

10) ______________________________

____

Money, Money, Money!

You may not have to worry about money right now, but money does make the world go around, as the song says, and it becomes more important as you grow older. How else are you going to get the new Fifa or the latest team strip? So let's see how you might manage money when you're older...

1) You win a small amount of money in a local lottery. Do you...

a) Go online immediately and it's gone in an hour?

b) Put it all into your savings?

c) Buy yourself something you've been needing/wanting for ages and put the rest into savings?

2) You're discussing the family holiday. Do you suggest...

a) A tropical beach holiday?

b) Camping in the UK?

c) Researching the internet for the best deals?

3) The latest games console is out. Do you...

a) Buy it immediately?

b) Decide against buying it?

c) Think about the fact that you already have a perfectly functioning games console, so you could save up over a year and get it then?

4) It's your mum's birthday coming up. Do you...

a) Buy her those expensive earrings she keeps looking at in town?

b) Make her something personal that shows you care?

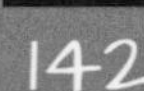

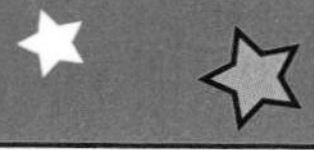

c) Put your money together with the rest of your family to buy the earrings as a joint present?

5) You and your friends have been planning see a new film at the weekend. Unfortunately, you realize you haven't got enough money. Do you...

a) Beg and borrow money off your next allowance from your parents?

b) Tell your friends that you can't make it and stay at home?

c) Ask them if they would mind having a DVD evening/ sleepover at yours this time?

6) You can't decide which of two pairs of football boots to buy. Do you...

a) Buy both pairs – you'll wear them eventually?

b) Buy the cheapest pair?

c) Buy the pair that you think will last you longer?

Mostly a): Money burns a hole in your pocket. Everyone loves treating themselves but learning not to spend to the max is good training for the future. Try to save a little each month so that you have money for treats without borrowing.

Mostly b): You are really cautious with your money and think carefully about whether you need something before buying it. These are all really good attributes to have and will help you stay out of debt in the future, but remember to treat yourself once in a while!

Mostly c): Congratulations! You are certainly in control of your money. You make sure you don't spend too much but you're still able to buy what you need by using your savings.

DON'T HATE HOMEWORK!

It's important to give yourself choices as you grow, achieved by working toward goals in school and college. This is helped by changing your mindset toward learning. If you stop fighting it, it can feel so rewarding! Learn to shrug off bad marks or a bad result – they are simply a tool to show you the way toward a better mark next time.

- Try to start the homework you have been given on the day it was set. Never wait until the night before it is due.
- Set up homework "dates" with a friend, either in person or online.
- Create a dedicated homework space in your house, somewhere you can leave your books out so you can carry on where you left off more easily.
- Use a timer. Say to yourself that you will spend half an hour on maths and then, whether you've finished or not, move onto another subject or do something else entirely – like playing football outside – coming back to maths at another time.
- Make yourself a snack and a drink.
- Make use of the many learning apps available and switch between working online and working offline.

BE POSITIVE AND GET HELP WHEN YOU NEED IT!

ALBERT EINSTEIN

MESSAGING THE FUTURE

Write a letter to your future self. This could be you in a year's time or you in a few years' time, say at the end of secondary school! Imagine who you would like to become. What kind of person do you want to be? What would you like people to think and say about you? This letter is private and should be a chance for you to open up about your thoughts, feelings and goals.

Things to include:

- What advice would you give yourself when starting something new?
- What would you like to change about yourself?
- How can you improve yourself?
- What are your ambitions?
- What are your goals?
- What are your dreams?
- Whom would you like to get to know?
- What new things would you like to take part in?

In the zone!

Do you prefer to huddle in your comfort zone or do you leap out of it at every opportunity? Complete this quiz to discover if you're a hothead or a hermit!

1) You trust your gut feelings.

☐ **True** ☐ **False** ☐ **I don't know** ☐ **Maybe**

2) You won't begin a new challenge unless you believe you are going to be awesome at it.

☐ **True** ☐ **False** ☐ **I don't know** ☐ **Maybe**

3) Your friends think you're a bit "out there"!

☐ **True** ☐ **False** ☐ **I don't know** ☐ **Maybe**

4) It's so difficult to deal with people who can't make up their minds!

☐ **True** ☐ **False** ☐ **I don't know** ☐ **Maybe**

5) You play games for fun and not for the sake of winning.

☐ **True** ☐ **False** ☐ **I don't know** ☐ **Maybe**

6) You hate change.

☐ **True** ☐ **False** ☐ **I don't know** ☐ **Maybe**

7) Usually you don't worry about your mistakes.

☐ **True** ☐ **False** ☐ **I don't know** ☐ **Maybe**

8) You will never do something that others haven't tried before you.

☐ **True** ☐ **False** ☐ **I don't know** ☐ **Maybe**

Scores

1)	a) 4	b) 1	c) 0	d) 2
2)	a) 1	b) 4	c) 0	d) 0
3)	a) 4	b) 1	c) 0	d) 2
4)	a) 2	b) 1	c) 0	d) 1
5)	a) 4	b) 1	c) 0	d) 2
6)	a) 1	b) 4	c) 0	d) 0
7)	a) 4	b) 1	c) 0	d) 2
8)	a) 1	b) 4	c) 0	d) 0

20–30: You are a thrill-seeking daredevil. You are very comfortable with taking risks and challenging your comfort zone, finding personal growth and much satisfaction!

10–20: You are fairly risk averse. Although you generally prefer to stay within your comfort zone, you venture out on occasion, gently stretching yourself and opening yourself up to new experiences. You consider your options carefully and then try to take the best possible decision while minimizing the chances of failure.

0–10: You prefer to always stay in your comfort zone and that's OK! Unwillingness to take risks is not necessarily cowardly and is a matter of preference. If you suspect, however, that some degree of fear is involved, and you would like to change, you can begin to stretch yourself gently by trying something new or by being around people who are comfortable with risk.

He who moves
a mountain
begins by
carrying away
small stones.

WHO DARES WINS!

Our comfort zone is where we feel safe: not stressed, not threatened in any way, just comfortable! Inside our comfort zone are things that feel familiar and easy for us. And what's outside our comfort zone is different for each of us.

Think about the many things you do without hesitation, like a walk with a friend, or playing a sport – all activities that make you feel at ease. While those things are fine and stepping out of your comfort zone may make you feel awkward, uneasy or even fearful, moving from the known and familiar into the unknown and unfamiliar can lead to many challenging but rewarding and fulfilling experiences – it's where the growth happens!

- To grow and excel, we must push our inner limits to "discomfort".
- Small jumps can drive large leaps.
- Every small step beyond your comfort zone expands it permanently!

As Eleanor Roosevelt (wife of the U.S. President Franklin D. Roosevelt) once very wisely said, "Do one thing every day that scares you." So... think about four things that scare you the most and write them below:

1) ____________________

____

2) ____________________

____

3) ____________________

____

4) ____________________

____

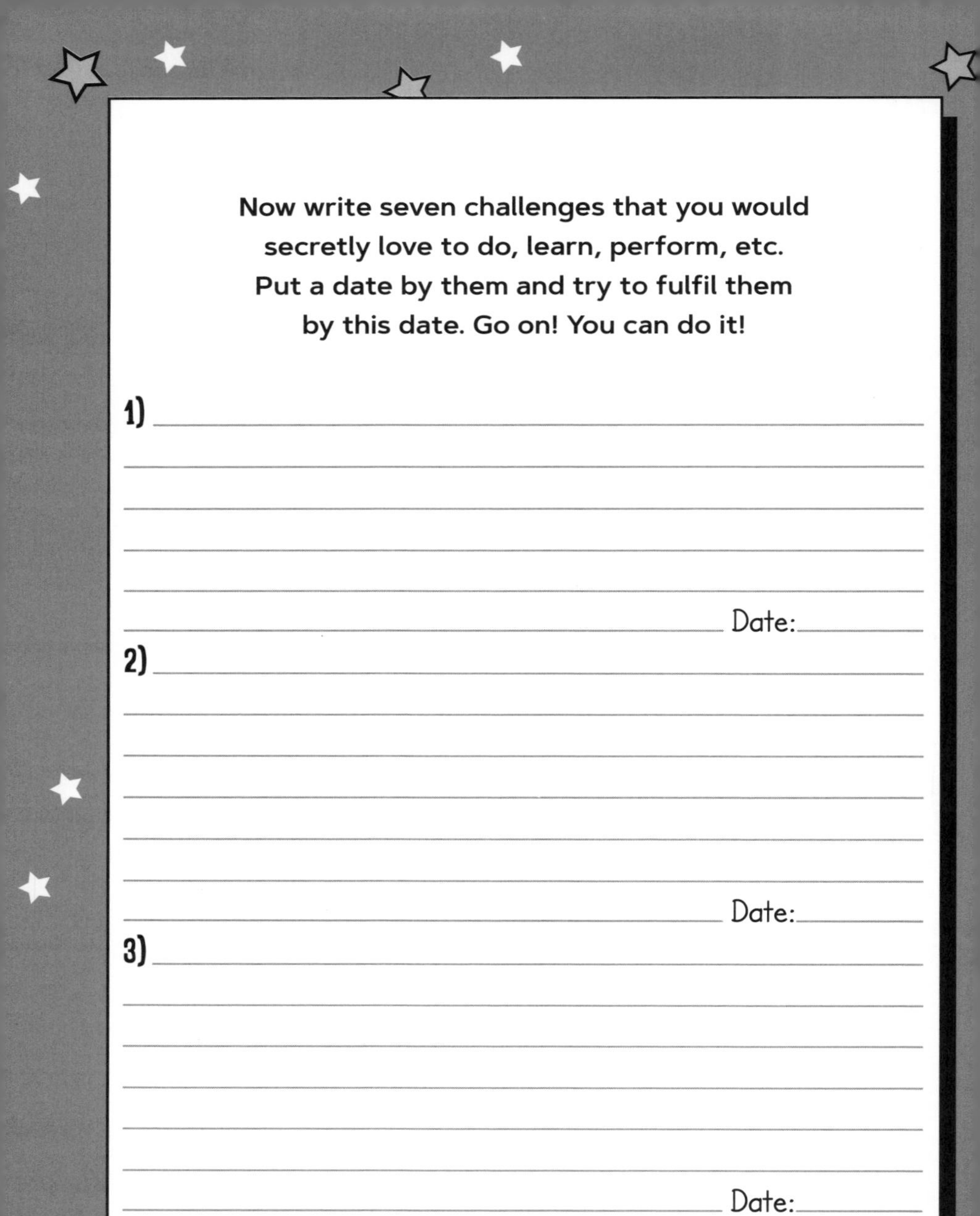

Now write seven challenges that you would secretly love to do, learn, perform, etc. Put a date by them and try to fulfil them by this date. Go on! You can do it!

1) ______________________________

____

____

____

____

______________________________ Date: __________

2) ______________________________

____

____

____

____

____

______________________________ Date: __________

3) ______________________________

____

____

____

____

____

______________________________ Date: __________

4)

Date:

5)

Date:

6)

Date:

7)

Date:

TICK THE HABIT!

Building an incredible future means building in good self-care habits like exercising regularly, eating healthily, drinking water and getting plenty of sleep. With a small amount of initial discipline, you can create a new habit that requires little effort to maintain.

Here is a tip for creating new habits and making them stick, called the 21/90 rule. Commit to a goal for 21 days. After three weeks, the pursuit of that goal should have become a habit. Once you've established that habit, continue to do it for another 90 days.

Fill in the monthly tracker on the opposite page to help you record your progress.

MONTH ____ YEAR ____

DAY	HABITS				
1					
2					
3					
4					
5					
6					
7					
8					
9					
10					
11					
12					
13					
14					
15					
16					
17					
18					
19					
20					
21					
22					
23					
24					
25					
26					
27					
28					
29					
30					
31					

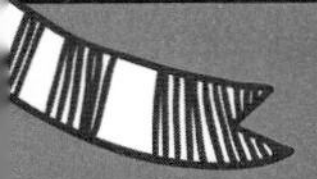

A–Z pop quiz

You have explored who you are and what makes you awesome! Now explore the world of trivia; some questions may need research and others you should know, but have fun trying!

1) What A is an insect that can carry up to 20 times its own body weight?
2) What B is a town on the south coast where George V stayed in order to recover from lung surgery?
3) What C is another word for your collar bone?
4) What D is an animal reputed to have been domesticated 23,000 years ago?
5) What E is the air, water and land in or on which people, animals and plants live?
6) What F is a common lilac flower that helps cure heart disease?
7) What G is an air-like substance that can move around freely or might flow to fit a container?
8) What H is celebrated on 31 October?
9) What I is the name of an indigenous person inhabiting the Arctic and sub-Arctic regions?
10) What J is what Americans call jam?
11) What K is another name for Father Christmas?
12) What L is a position on the football pitch?
13) What M is the capital of Russia?
14) What N is a commonly used spice native to Indonesia?

15) What O is how Americans describe attack in sports?

16) What P is the leader of the UK government?

17) What Q is historical slang for doctors?

18) What R is a primary colour?

19) What S is the planet in our solar system with visible rings?

20) What T is a five-day cricket match?

21) What U is the name of the "referee" in tennis and cricket?

22) What V is a German car manufacturer meaning "people's car"?

23) What W is a football team that plays at Vicarage Road?

24) What X is a percussion instrument?

25) What Y is an animal found throughout the Himalayan region?

26) Which Zs are countries in Africa? (There are two.)

Answers

Ant
Bognor
Clavicle
Dog
Environment
Foxglove
Gas
Halloween
Inuit
Jelly
Kris Kringle
Left field/Left back
Moscow
Nutmeg
Offence
Prime minister
Quack
Red
Saturn
Test
Umpire
Volkswagen (VW)
Watford
Xylophone
Yak
Zambia and Zimbabwe

Conclusion

You are at the end of your journey of self-discovery – although you will soon discover that you will be learning new things about yourself for your entire life! You have a much better understanding of your unique place in the world and the positive changes that you can make to it. Your talents, your skills and your dreams are all you need to become the most remarkable you.

Remember to take a chance and trust yourself to make good choices. Always ask questions and don't let anyone off the hook if you are not feeling heard! Chart your own course and destiny because following the well-trodden path will take you on someone else's journey.

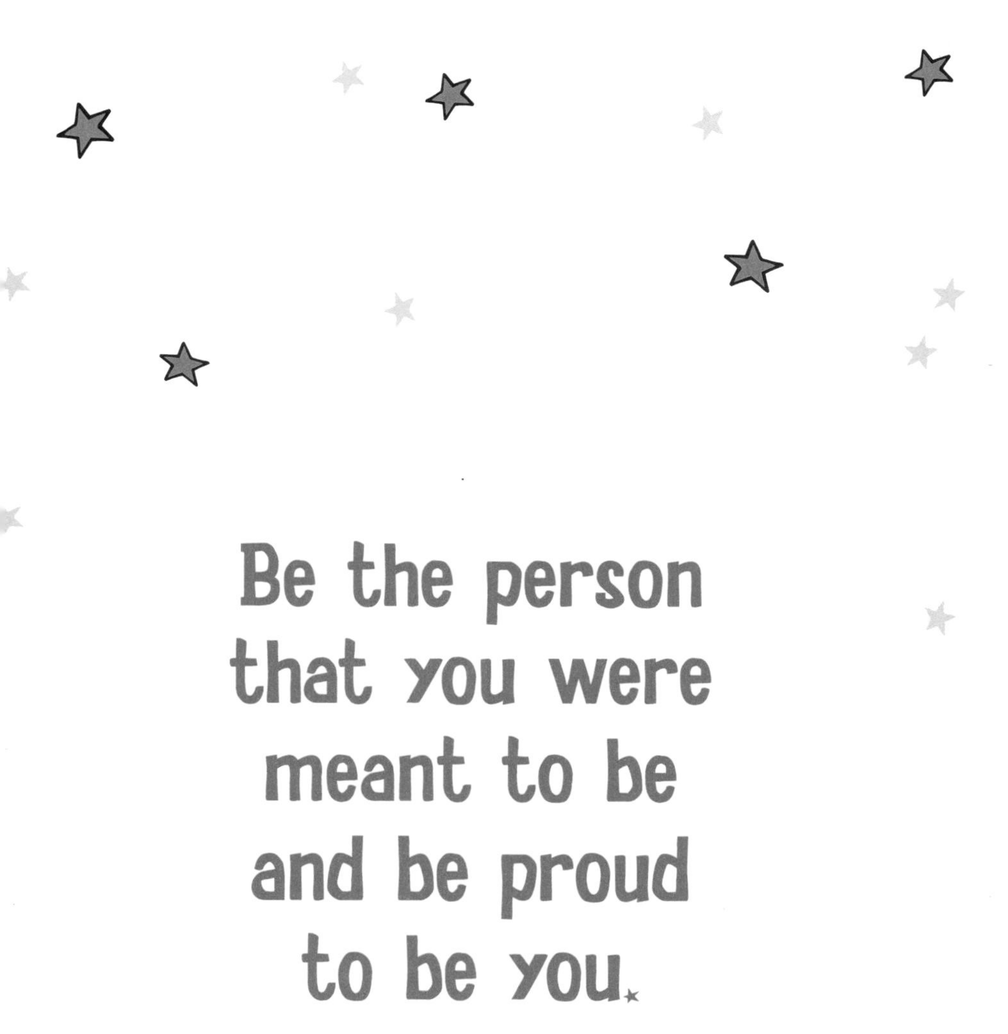

Be the person
that you were
meant to be
and be proud
to be you.

Have you enjoyed this book?

If so, why not write a review on your favourite website?

If you're interested in finding out more about our books, find us on Facebook at **Summersdale Publishers**, on Twitter at **@Summersdale** and on Instagram at **@summersdalebooks** and get in touch. We'd love to hear from you!

Thanks very much for buying this Summersdale book.

www.summersdale.com

Image credits

pp.1, 3, 10, 16, 42, 46, 70, 87, 96, 115, 126, 145 - shield © smallsketch/Shutterstock.com; pp.8-9, 25, 36-37, 38-39, 47, 52-53, 72-73, 86, 95, 114, 120-121, 136, 141, 158-159, 160 - stars © blue67design/Shutterstock.com; p.19 characters © Tasty_Cat/Shutterstock.com; pp.20-23, 32, 40-41, 92-93, 98-99, 108-109, 118-119, 138-139, 146-147 © Miloje/Shutterstock.com; pp.20-23 - sports doodles © mhatzapa/Shutterstock.com; p.24 - background © gn8/Shutterstock.com; pp.28, 50, 76-77, 101, 106-107, 140, 148-149 - background © pzAxe/Shutterstock.com; p.32 - lavender © Irina Vaneeva/Shutterstock.com; pp.38, 64-65, 76-77, 84-85, 156-157 - question marks © Receh Lancar Jaya/Shutterstock.com; pp.44-45 - doodles © Aniwhite/Shutterstock.com; p.47 - books © topform/Shutterstock.com; pp.48-49 © mkvolkova/Shutterstock.com; p.54 - footballs © balabolka/Shutterstock.com; goal © Vector street/Shutterstock.com; pp.55-57 © Kudryashka/Shutterstock.com; p.59 - clouds © marssanya/Shutterstock.com; p.58 © Polina/Shutterstock.com; p.78 - bag © TrifoncoIvan /Shutterstock.com; pp.80-81 - map © Vanatchanan/Shutterstock.com; p.86 - food © anne celine moisan/Shutterstock.com; p.104 - thought/speech bubbles © Receh Lancar Jaya/Shutterstock.com; pp.110-113 - doodles © mhatzapa/Shutterstock.com; p.125 © marssanya/Shutterstock.com; p.131 - award © Netkoff/Shutterstock.com; movie bits © balabolka/Shutterstock.com; other doodles © topform, Erik D, orveef, Anastacia - azzzya, Irina Adamovich, HelenField, Polina/Shutterstock.com